P16

Collins

Homework Book, Foundation 1

Delivering the Edexcel Specification

NEW GCSE MATHS
Edexcel Linear

Fully supports the 2010 GCSE Specification

Name	Form
Nichole Bitoga	9W

Brian Speed • Keith Gordon • Kevin Evans • Trevor Senior

CONTENTS

INTRODUCTION

Welcome to Collins New GCSE Maths for Edexcel Linear Foundation Homework Book 1. This book follows the structure of the Edexcel Linear Foundation Student Book.

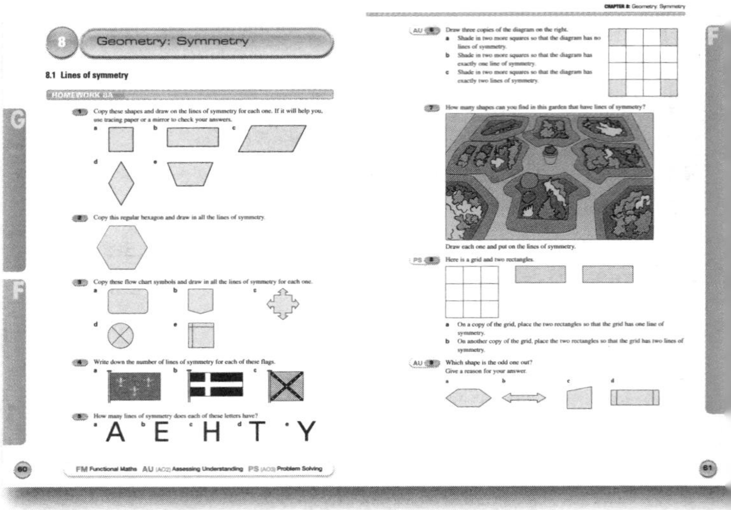

Colour-coded grades

Know what target grade you are working at and track your progress with the colour-coded grade panels at the side of the page.

Use of calculators

Questions when you could use a calculator are marked with a  icon.

Examples

Recap on methods you need by reading through the examples before starting the homework exercises.

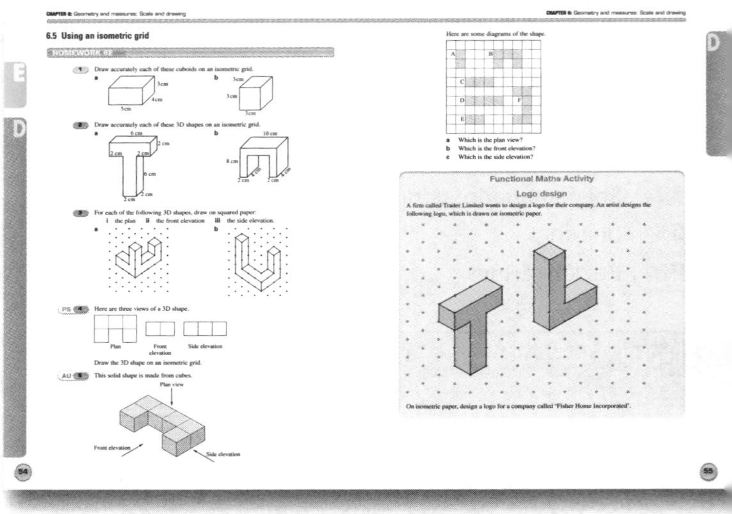

Functional maths

Practise functional maths skills to see how people use maths in everyday life. Look out for practice questions marked FM.

There are also extra functional maths and problem-solving activities at the end of every chapter to build and apply your skills.

New Assessment Objectives

Practise new parts of the curriculum (Assessment Objectives AO2 and AO3) with questions that assess your understanding marked AU and questions that test if you can solve problems marked PS. You will also practise some questions that involve several steps and where you have to choose which method to use; these also test AO2. There are also plenty of straightforward questions (AO1) that test if you can do the maths.

Student Book CD-ROM

Remind yourself of the work covered in class with the Student Book in electronic form on the CD-ROM. Insert the CD into your machine and choose the chapter you need.

1 Number: Basic number

1.1 Adding with grids

HOMEWORK 1A

1 Find the row and column sums of each of these grids.

a

2	5	1	□
8	3	4	□
9	7	6	□
□	□	□	□

b

3	0	1	□
7	5	6	□
8	4	2	□
□	□	□	□

c

0	3	5	□
9	6	8	□
2	7	1	□
□	□	□	□

d

3	1	8	□
6	2	0	□
7	9	4	□
□	□	□	□

e

8	1	3	□
6	4	5	□
2	7	0	□
□	□	□	□

2 **a** Jack has six pens, four pencils and two rulers. How many items has he altogether?

b Hannah has an aquarium. The fish she has are four guppies, three neon tetras and five goldfish.
How many fish does she have altogether?

AU **3** Here is a list of numbers.

1 4 5 8 9 10

a From the list, write down **two** numbers that add up to 17.

b From the list, work out the largest total that can be made using **three** numbers.

c From the list, work out the largest **even** total that can be made using **three** numbers.

4 Asif has a £10 note, two £5 notes, a £2 coin and four £1 coins. His bus fare home is £1.80. Can he afford a shirt costing £25 and still catch the bus?

5 Find the numbers missing from each of these grids. Remember: the numbers missing from each grid must be chosen from 0 to 9 without any repeats.

a

1	5	□	10
8	□	7	17
□	9	6	18
12	16	17	45

b

4	□	5	10
□	6	□	8
7	8	□	18
13	15	8	36

c

□	□	□	14
0	9	8	17
2	□	5	10
9	18	14	□

d

4	□	□	12
□	0	5	12
□	8	3	□
12	□	10	36

e

□	□	3	10
□	0	□	□
8	2	□	15
16	□	12	□

PS **6** Find **three different** numbers that add up to 23.

PS **7** Find **two different odd** numbers that add up to 28.

1.2 Multiplication tables check

HOMEWORK 1B

G

1 Write down the answer to each of the following without looking at a multiplication square.

a 4×3 **b** 7×4 **c** 6×5 **d** 3×8 **e** 8×6
f 9×4 **g** 5×9 **h** 9×7 **i** 8×8 **j** 9×8
k 7×6 **l** 7×7 **m** 4×6 **n** 8×7 **o** 5×5

2 Jane works for 7 hours and is paid £9 an hour. How much is she paid?

3 Write down the answer to each of the following without looking at a multiplication square.

a $14 \div 2$ **b** $28 \div 4$ **c** $24 \div 6$ **d** $20 \div 5$ **e** $18 \div 3$
f $35 \div 5$ **g** $27 \div 3$ **h** $32 \div 4$ **i** $24 \div 8$ **j** $21 \div 7$
k $42 \div 6$ **l** $40 \div 8$ **m** $18 \div 9$ **n** $49 \div 7$ **o** $48 \div 6$

4 Phil works for 6 hours and is paid £36. How much is he paid for each hour?

5 Write down the answer to each of the following. Look carefully at the signs, because they are a mixture of +, –, × and ÷.

a $8 + 5$ **b** $20 - 6$ **c** 4×5 **d** $16 \div 4$ **e** $14 - 8$
f $15 \div 3$ **g** $16 + 8$ **h** 5×7 **i** $16 + 5$ **j** $36 \div 6$
k $17 - 8$ **l** 9×3 **m** $42 \div 7$ **n** 6×9 **o** $21 - 6$

FM 6 Fatima works for 2 hours and is paid £12 an hour. Andy works for 3 hours and is paid £9 an hour. Who is paid the most?

AU 7 Here are four single-digit number cards.

2	8	4	5

The cards are used for making calculations.
Complete the following.

a 51 + ... = 135
b 95 – .... = 50
c .... 7 + ... = 332

8 Write down the answer to each of the following.

a 4×10 **b** 7×10 **c** 9×10 **d** 11×10 **e** 3×100
f 5×100 **g** 24×100 **h** 45×100 **i** $80 \div 10$ **j** $130 \div 10$
k $510 \div 10$ **l** $1000 \div 10$ **m** $700 \div 100$ **n** $900 \div 100$ **o** $1200 \div 100$

F

PS 9 **a** Two consecutive numbers, when added together, give an answer of 21. What is the even number?

b Two whole numbers, when divided, give an answer of 15. One of the numbers is 4. What is the other number?

1.3 Order of operations and BIDMAS/BODMAS

HOMEWORK 1C

G

1 Work out each of these.

a $3 \times 4 + 7 =$ **b** $8 + 2 \times 4 =$ **c** $12 \div 3 + 4 =$ **d** $10 - 8 \div 2 =$
e $7 + 2 - 3 =$ **f** $5 \times 4 - 8 =$ **g** $9 + 10 \div 5 =$ **h** $11 - 9 \div 1 =$
i $12 \div 1 - 6 =$ **j** $4 + 4 \times 4 =$ **k** $10 \div 2 + 8 =$ **l** $6 \times 3 - 5 =$

G

2 Work out each of these. Remember: first work out the bracket.

a	$3 \times (2 + 4) =$	b	$12 \div (4 + 2) =$	c	$(4 + 6) \div 5 =$
d	$(10 - 6) + 5 =$	e	$3 \times (9 \div 3) =$	f	$5 + (4 \times 2) =$
g	$(5 + 3) \div 2 =$	h	$(5 \div 1) \times 4 =$	i	$(7 - 4) \times (1 + 4) =$
j	$(7 + 5) \div (6 - 3) =$	k	$(8 - 2) \div (2 + 1) =$	l	$15 \div (15 - 12) =$

3 Copy each of these and then put in brackets to make each sum true.

a	$4 \times 5 - 1 = 16$	b	$8 \div 2 + 4 = 8$	c	$8 - 3 \times 4 = 20$	d	$12 - 5 \times 2 = 2$
e	$3 \times 3 + 2 = 15$	f	$12 \div 2 + 1 = 4$	g	$9 \times 6 \div 3 = 18$	h	$20 - 8 + 5 = 7$
i	$6 + 4 \div 2 = 5$	j	$16 \div 4 \div 2 = 8$	k	$20 \div 2 + 2 = 12$	l	$5 \times 3 - 5 = 10$

AU 4 Jo says that $8 - 3 \times 2$ is equal to 10.
Show that Jo is wrong.

F

5 Put any of +, –, ×, ÷ or ( ) in each sum to make it true.

a	2 5 10 = 0	b	10 2 5 = 1	c	10 5 2 = 3	d	10 2 5 = 4
e	10 5 2 = 7	f	5 10 2 = 10	g	10 5 2 = 13	h	5 10 2 = 17
i	10 2 5 = 20	j	5 10 2 = 25	k	2 2 2 = 2		

AU 6 Amanda worked out $3 + 4 \times 5$ and got the answer 35. Andrew worked out $3 + 4 \times 5$ and got the answer 23. Explain why they got different answers.

AU 7 You have to explain to someone how to work out this calculation.
$7 + 2 \times 6$
Write down what you would say.

PS 8 Here is a list of numbers, some symbols and one pair of brackets.
2 5 6 42 + × = ( )
Use all of them to make a correct calculation.

PS 9 Here is a list of numbers, some symbols and one pair of brackets.
1 3 5 8 – ÷ = ( )
Use all of them to make a correct calculation.

FM 10 Jon has a piece of wood that is 8 metres long.

He wants to use his calculator to work out how much is left when he cuts off three pieces, each of length 1.2 metres.

Which calculation would give him the correct answer?

i $8 - 1.2 - 1.2 - 1.2$
ii $8 - 1.2 \times 3$
iii $8 - 1.2 + 1.2 + 1.2$

1.4 Place value and ordering numbers

HOMEWORK 1D

G

1 Write the value of each underlined digit.

a	$5\underline{7}6$	b	$37\underline{4}$	c	$\underline{6}89$	d	$\underline{4}785$	e	$300\underline{7}$
f	$7\underline{6}08$	g	$354\underline{2}$	h	$1\underline{2}\,745$	i	$\underline{8}7\,409$	j	$\underline{7}\,777\,777$

2 Write each of the following using just words.

a 7245 b 9072 c 29 450 d 2 760 000 e 5 800 000

3 Write each of the following using digits only.

a Eight thousand and five hundred
b Forty two thousand and forty two
c Six million
d Five million and five

G

4 Write these numbers in order, putting the **smallest** first.

a 31, 20, 14, 22, 8, 25, 30, 12

b 159, 155, 176, 167, 170, 168, 151, 172

c 2100, 2070, 2002, 1990, 2010, 1998, 2000, 2092

5 Write these numbers in order, putting the **largest** first.

a 49, 62, 75, 57, 50, 72

b 988, 1052, 999, 1010, 980, 1007

c 4567, 4765, 4675, 4576, 4657, 4756

FM 6 Here are the distances from home to five seaside towns.

Skegness (86 miles)
Rhyl (115 miles)
Great Yarmouth (166 miles)
Scarborough (80 miles)
Blackpool (105 miles)

a Which place is the furthest from home?

b Which place is the nearest to home?

PS 7 Using each of the digits 7, 8 and 9 only once in each number:

a write as many three-digit numbers as you can.

b which of your numbers is the smallest?

c which of your numbers is the largest?

PS 8 Write down in order of size, largest first, all the two-digit numbers that can be made using 2, 4 and 6. (Each digit can be repeated.)

9 Copy each of these sentences, writing the numbers in words.

a The diameter of the Earth at the equator is 12 756 kilometres.

b The Moon is approximately 238 000 miles from the Earth.

c The greatest distance of the Earth from the Sun is 94 600 000 miles.

F

AU 10 Using each of the digits 1, 5, 6 and 9, make a four-digit even number greater than eight thousand.

1.5 Rounding

HOMEWORK 1E

G

1 Round each of these numbers to the nearest 10.

a	34	**b**	67	**c**	23	**d**	49	**e**	55
f	11	**g**	95	**h**	123	**i**	109	**j**	125

2 Round each of these numbers to the nearest 100.

a	231	**b**	389	**c**	410	**d**	777	**e**	850
f	117	**g**	585	**h**	250	**i**	975	**j**	1245

3 Round each of these numbers to the nearest 1000.

a	2176	**b**	3800	**c**	6760	**d**	4455	**e**	1204
f	6782	**g**	5500	**h**	8808	**i**	1500	**j**	9999

4 The selling prices of five houses in a village are as follows:

FOR SALE **£8400**	FOR SALE **£12 900**	FOR SALE **£45 300**	FOR SALE **£75 550**	FOR SALE **£99 500**

Give the prices to the nearest thousand pounds.

G

5 Give these bus journey times to the nearest 5 minutes.

a 16 minutes **b** 28 minutes **c** 34 minutes **d** 42 minutes
e $23\frac{1}{2}$ minutes **f** $17\frac{1}{2}$ minutes

6 Mark knows that he has £240 in his savings account to the nearest ten pounds.

a What is the smallest amount that he could have?
b What is the greatest amount that he could have?

7 The size of a crowd at an open-air pop festival was reported to be 8000 to the nearest thousand.

a What is the lowest number that the crowd could be?
b What is the largest number that the crowd could be?

FM 8 An estate agent values houses and rounds the value to the nearest £1000 for an advert and then subtracts £5.
A house is valued at £89 600
How much does the advert say?

PS 9 Mutasem and Ruba are playing a game with whole numbers.

a Mutasem says, "I am thinking of a number. Rounded to the nearest 10, it is 270. What is the biggest number I could be thinking of?"
b Ruba says, "I am thinking of a different number. Rounded to the nearest 100, it is 300. It is less than 270. How many possible answers are there?"

F

PS 10 The number of fish in a pond is 130 to the nearest 10.
The number of frogs in the pond is 90 to the nearest 10.
Show how there could be 230 fish and frogs altogether in the pond.

1.6 Adding and subtracting numbers with up to four digits

HOMEWORK 1F

G

1 Copy and work out each of these additions.

a $\begin{array}{r} 75 \\ +\ 23 \\ \hline \end{array}$ **b** $\begin{array}{r} 245 \\ +\ 156 \\ \hline \end{array}$ **c** $\begin{array}{r} 307 \\ +\ 293 \\ \hline \end{array}$ **d** $\begin{array}{r} 4158 \\ +\ 3951 \\ \hline \end{array}$ **e** $\begin{array}{r} 4289 \\ 532 \\ +\ \ 96 \\ \hline \end{array}$

2 Complete each of these additions.

a 25 + 89 + 12 **b** 211 + 385 + 46 **c** 125 + 88 + 720
d 478 + 207 + 300 **e** 1275 + 3245 + 524

3 Copy and complete each of these subtractions.

a $\begin{array}{r} 354 \\ -120 \\ \hline \end{array}$ **b** $\begin{array}{r} 651 \\ -128 \\ \hline \end{array}$ **c** $\begin{array}{r} 785 \\ -207 \\ \hline \end{array}$ **d** $\begin{array}{r} 450 \\ -178 \\ \hline \end{array}$ **e** $\begin{array}{r} 5421 \\ -2568 \\ \hline \end{array}$

4 Complete each of these subtractions.

a 386 – 296 **b** 709 – 518 **c** 452 – 386
d 800 – 258 **e** 7208 – 1564

FM 5 The train from Brighton to London takes 68 minutes.
The train from London to Birmingham takes 85 minutes.

a How long does it take to travel from Brighton to London and then London to Birmingham altogether, if there is a 30-minute wait between trains in London?
b How much longer does the train take from London to Birmingham than from Brighton to London?

AU 6 Michael is checking the addition of two numbers.
His answer is 917.
One of the numbers is 482.
What should the other number be?

PS 7 Copy each of these and fill in the missing digits.

a
```
  4 5
+ 3 □
-----
  □ 7
```
b
```
  □ 7
+ 4 □
-----
  9 2
```
c
```
  3 □ 4
+ 2 8 6
-------
  □ 4 □
```
d
```
  □ □ □
+ 2 8 7
-------
  5 5 5
```

PS 8 Copy each of these and fill in the missing digits.

a
```
  7 5
- 1 □
-----
  □ 3
```
b
```
  3 2 □
- 1 □ 4
-------
  1 8 2
```
c
```
  5 8 3
- □ □ □
-------
  1 3 5
```
d
```
  □ □ □
- 2 4 8
-------
  3 7 4
```

1.7 Multiplying and dividing by single-digit numbers

HOMEWORK 1G

1 Copy and work out each of the following.

a
```
  24
× 3
```
b
```
  38
× 4
```
c
```
  124
×   5
```
d
```
  408
×   6
```
e
```
  359
×   8
```

2 Calculate each of these multiplications.

a 21×5 **b** 37×7 **c** 203×9 **d** 4×876 **e** 6×3214

3 Alex, Peter and Theo are footballers.
The manager of their club has offered them a bonus of £5 for every goal they score.

Alex scores 15 goals
Peter scores 12 goals
Theo scores 20 goals

a How many goals do they score altogether?
b How much bonus does each footballer receive?

4 Calculate each of these divisions.

a $684 \div 2$ **b** $525 \div 3$ **c** $804 \div 4$ **d** $7260 \div 5$ **e** $2560 \div 8$

PS FM 5 The footballers in question 3 are given a goals target for the following season.
The manager wants the total of the goals target to add up to 55, with Theo having the highest target and Peter the lowest.
Show how this can be done.

	Goals Target
Alex	
Peter	
Theo	
	Total = 55

6 By doing a suitable multiplication, answer each of these questions.

a How many people could seven 55-seater coaches hold?
b Adam buys seven postcards at 23p each. How much does he spend in pounds?
c Nails are packed in boxes of 144. How many nails are there in five boxes?
d Eight people book a holiday, costing £284 each. What is the total cost?
e How many yards are there in six miles if there are 1760 yards in a mile?

7 By doing a suitable division, answer each of these questions.

a In a school there are 288 students in eight forms in Year 10. If there are the same number of students in each form, how many students are there in each one?

b Phil jogs seven miles every morning. How many days will it take him to cover a total distance of 441 miles?

c In a supermarket, cans of cola are sold in packs of six. If there are 750 cans on the shelf, how many packs are there?

d Sandra's wages for a month were £2060. Assuming there are four weeks in a month, how much does she earn in a week?

e Tickets for a charity disco were sold at £5 each. How many people bought tickets if the total sales were £1710?

Functional Maths Activity

Hairdressing

The prices at the hairdressers change according to the amount of experience that the hairdresser has. Stylists charge the least and senior technicians charge the most.

Cut & finishing prices:	Stylists	Senior stylists	Senior Technicians
Ladies' cut & blow dry	£23	£31	£36
Ladies' restyle	£26	£33	£38
Ladies' blow dry	£15	£17	£18
Ladies' hair up	–	£25	£25
Men's cut & finish	£12	£18	£24
Boys	£8	£10	–

Special Offer

Wednesdays only

Pensioners £5 off when spending £20 or less

£10 off when spending more than £20

Technical prices:	Stylists	Senior stylists	Senior Technicians
Highlights Foil (full head)	£51	£60	£67
Highlights Foil (half head)	£39	£45	£52
Highlights Foil (partial from...)	£15	£20	£20
Tinting (full head)	£39	£43	£50
Tinting (re-growth)	£34	£38	£42
Permanent Waving (from...)	£45	£50	£57

The Cutts family visit the hairdressers on a Wednesday.

Work out how much it will cost for each person.

How much do they save by going on Wednesday?

Do the same for your own family by deciding which haircuts to give them:

- Choose at least four members of your family.
- Decide which day of the week to go to the hairdressers.
- Do not make the same choices as the Cutts family.
- At least one of your choices should use the senior technician.

2 Number: Fractions

2.1 Recognise a fraction of a shape

HOMEWORK 2A

1 What fraction is shaded in each of these diagrams?

a
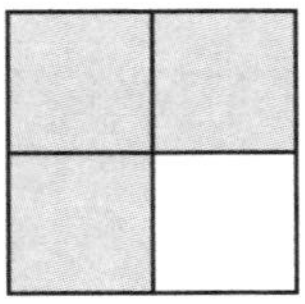

b
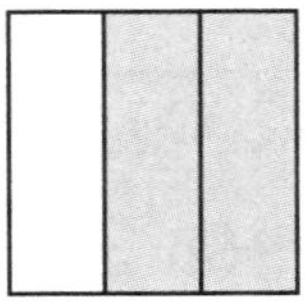

c
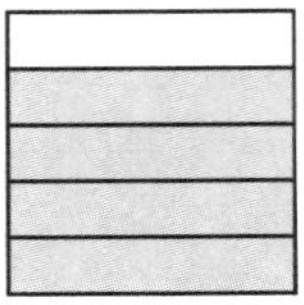

d
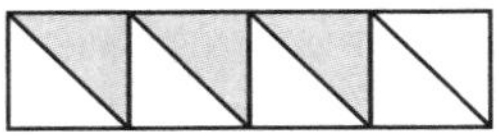

e
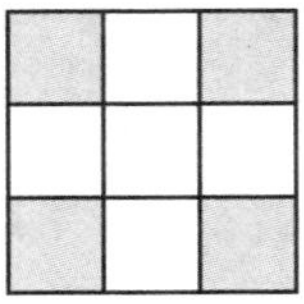

f
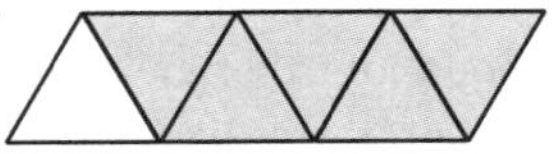

g
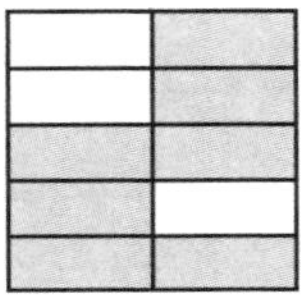

h
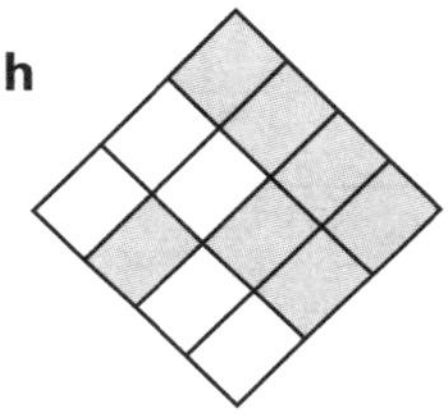

2 Draw diagrams as in Question **1** to show these fractions.

a $\frac{1}{3}$ **b** $\frac{3}{5}$ **c** $\frac{7}{10}$ **d** $\frac{5}{8}$ **e** $\frac{7}{9}$

f $\frac{3}{7}$ **g** $\frac{5}{12}$ **h** $\frac{7}{15}$

PS 3 Look again at the diagrams in Question **1**.
For each of the following pairs of diagrams, decide which diagram has the greater proportion shaded.

i b and e
ii a and d
iii c and g

FM 4 A dressmaker cuts a piece of cloth into two equal parts. She then cuts one of the parts into two equal parts.

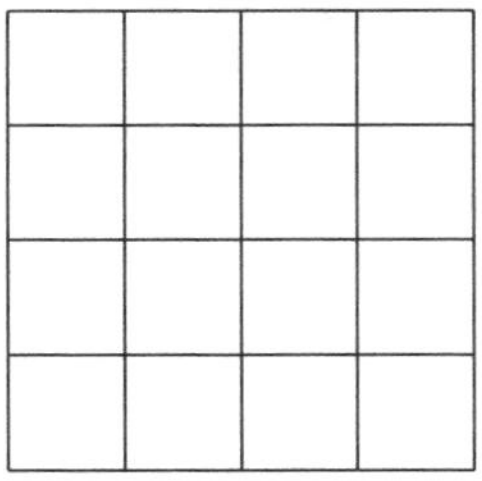

Make two copies of the grid above and show two different ways that she can do this by shading the smaller area in each case.

AU 5 Here are three grids A, B and C.

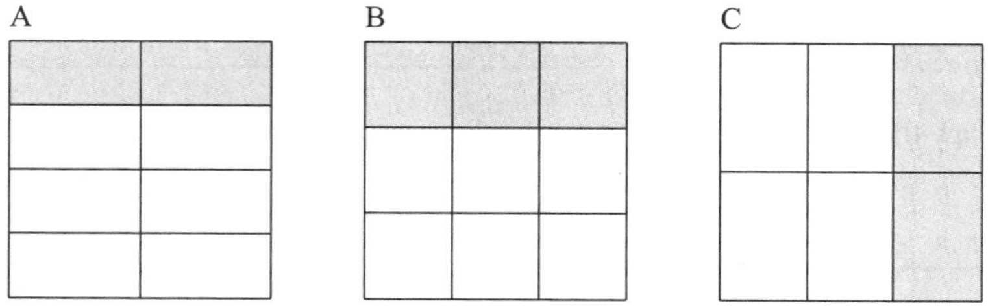

Give a reason why grid B could be the odd one out.

2.2 Adding and subtracting simple fractions

HOMEWORK 2B

Example **a** $\frac{5}{12} + \frac{4}{12} = \frac{9}{12}$

b $\frac{7}{10} - \frac{3}{10} = \frac{4}{10}$

1 Calculate each of the following.

a $\frac{1}{4} + \frac{1}{4}$ **b** $\frac{2}{5} + \frac{1}{5}$ **c** $\frac{3}{7} + \frac{2}{7}$ **d** $\frac{5}{8} + \frac{1}{8}$ **e** $\frac{5}{6} + \frac{2}{6}$

f $\frac{4}{9} + \frac{4}{9}$ **g** $\frac{3}{10} + \frac{4}{10}$ **h** $\frac{2}{5} + \frac{2}{5}$ **i** $\frac{4}{12} + \frac{1}{12}$ **j** $\frac{5}{20} + \frac{7}{20}$

2 Calculate each of the following.

a $\frac{4}{5} - \frac{2}{5}$ **b** $\frac{5}{8} - \frac{1}{8}$ **c** $\frac{6}{7} - \frac{2}{7}$ **d** $\frac{8}{10} - \frac{3}{10}$ **e** $\frac{5}{6} - \frac{3}{6}$

f $\frac{7}{9} - \frac{3}{9}$ **g** $\frac{7}{8} - \frac{1}{8}$ **h** $\frac{4}{9} - \frac{2}{9}$ **i** $\frac{7}{12} - \frac{5}{12}$ **j** $\frac{11}{20} - \frac{3}{20}$

PS 3 **a** Draw two diagrams to show $\frac{4}{8}$ and $\frac{2}{8}$.

b Show on your diagrams that $\frac{4}{8} = \frac{1}{2}$ and $\frac{2}{8} = \frac{1}{4}$.

c Use the above information to write down the answers to each of the following.

i $\frac{1}{2} + \frac{1}{8}$ **ii** $\frac{1}{2} + \frac{3}{8}$ **iii** $\frac{1}{4} + \frac{1}{8}$ **iv** $\frac{3}{4} + \frac{1}{8}$ **v** $\frac{1}{2} - \frac{1}{8}$ **vi** $\frac{1}{2} - \frac{3}{8}$ **vii** $\frac{1}{4} - \frac{1}{8}$ **viii** $\frac{3}{4} - \frac{1}{8}$

AU 4 Copy the diagrams below, shade them to show the working for this question and then write down the answer.

$\frac{1}{6} + \frac{1}{3} =$ ....

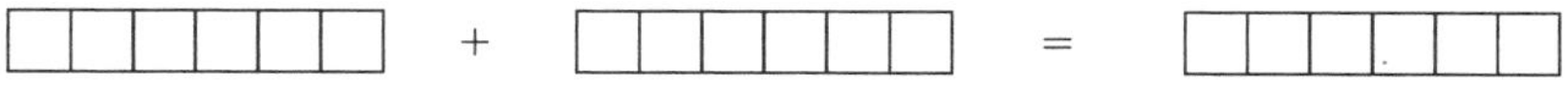

FM 5 There are ten people at a bus stop.

Six get on a bus but four other people arrive.

a How many people have been at the bus stop?

b What fraction of all these people are now at the bus stop?

c A man is giving away 100 free newspapers at the bus stop.
Every 10 minutes 15 people arrive at the bus stop and half of them take a paper.
How long will it take him to give away all the papers?

2.3 Recognise equivalent fractions, using diagrams

HOMEWORK 2C

1 Copy the diagram and use it to write down each of these fractions as tenths.

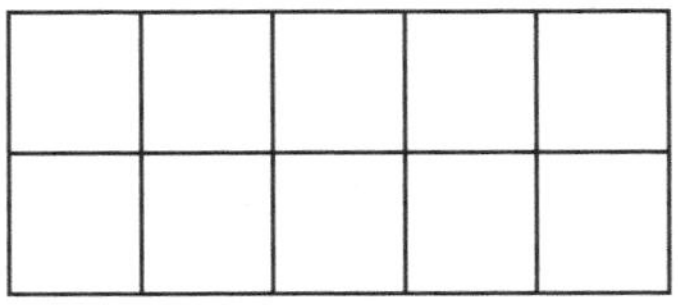

a $\frac{1}{2}$ **b** $\frac{1}{5}$ **c** $\frac{2}{5}$ **d** $\frac{3}{5}$ **e** $\frac{4}{5}$

2 Use your answers to Question **1** to write down the answer to each of the following. Each answer will be expressed in tenths.

a $\frac{1}{2} + \frac{1}{5}$ **b** $\frac{1}{2} + \frac{3}{10}$ **c** $\frac{2}{5} + \frac{1}{10}$ **d** $\frac{1}{5} + \frac{7}{10}$ **e** $\frac{1}{2} - \frac{2}{5}$ **f** $\frac{9}{10} - \frac{3}{5}$

3 Copy the diagram and use it to write down each of these fractions as twelfths.

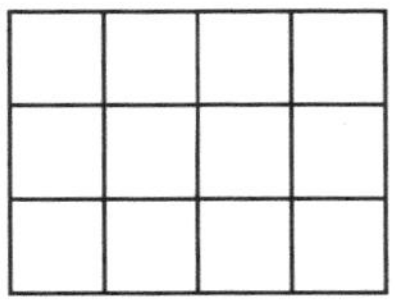

a $\frac{1}{2}$ **b** $\frac{1}{4}$ **c** $\frac{1}{3}$ **d** $\frac{3}{4}$ **e** $\frac{2}{3}$

4 Use your answers to Question **3** to write down the answer to each of the following. Each answer will be expressed in twelfths.

a $\frac{1}{2} + \frac{1}{3}$ **b** $\frac{1}{4} + \frac{1}{3}$ **c** $\frac{2}{3} + \frac{1}{4}$ **d** $\frac{1}{4} + \frac{7}{12}$ **e** $\frac{5}{12} + \frac{1}{2}$

f $\frac{2}{3} - \frac{1}{2}$ **g** $\frac{3}{4} - \frac{1}{3}$ **h** $\frac{1}{2} - \frac{1}{12}$ **i** $\frac{3}{4} - \frac{5}{12}$ **j** $\frac{2}{3} - \frac{7}{12}$

PS **5** Use the grid to decide which of the following fractions is the odd one out.

$\frac{5}{6}$ $\frac{3}{4}$ $\frac{10}{12}$

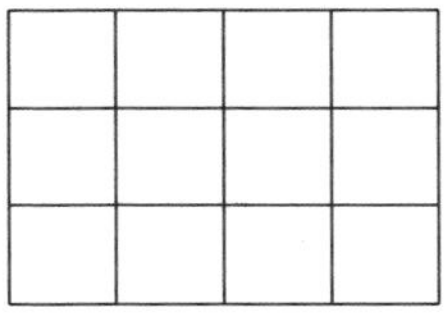

AU **6** Here is a multiplication table.

×	2	3	4	5
3	6	9	12	15
5	10	15	20	25

a Use the table to write down three more fractions that are equivalent to $\frac{3}{5}$.

b Extend this method to write down a different fraction that is equivalent to $\frac{3}{5}$.

FM **7** **a** Use a copy of the grid in Question **5** to write down the answer to $\frac{1}{4} + \frac{1}{12}$.

b A man has £120.
He gives one-quarter of it to his wife and one-twelfth to his son.
He gives the rest to his daughter. She see a dress advertised at half price. The normal price is £150. Will she be able to afford it?

2.4 Equivalent fractions and simplifying fractions by cancelling

HOMEWORK 2D

Example 1 Show $\frac{2}{3}$ is equivalent to $\frac{8}{12}$.

$$\frac{2}{3} \Rightarrow \frac{\times 4}{\times 4} = \frac{8}{12}$$

Example 2 Cancel down $\frac{15}{20}$ to its simplest form.

$$\frac{15}{20} \Rightarrow \frac{\div 5}{\div 5} = \frac{3}{4}$$

Example 3 Put these fractions in order with the smallest first: $\frac{5}{6}$ $\frac{2}{3}$ $\frac{3}{4}$.

By equivalent fractions $\frac{5}{6} = \frac{10}{12}$ $\frac{2}{3} = \frac{8}{12}$ $\frac{3}{4} = \frac{9}{12}$

Putting in order: $\frac{2}{3}$ $\frac{3}{4}$ $\frac{5}{6}$

1 Copy and complete each of these statements.

a $\frac{1}{4} \Rightarrow \frac{\times 3}{\times 3} = \frac{\ }{12}$ **b** $\frac{3}{5} \Rightarrow \frac{\times 4}{\times 4} = \frac{\ }{20}$ **c** $\frac{5}{8} \Rightarrow \frac{\times 2}{\times 2} = \frac{\ }{16}$ **d** $\frac{4}{7} \Rightarrow \frac{\times 3}{\times 3} = \frac{12}{\ }$

e $\frac{2}{3} \Rightarrow \frac{\times}{\times 5} = \frac{\ }{15}$ **f** $\frac{5}{9} \Rightarrow \frac{\times}{\times 2} = \frac{\ }{18}$ **g** $\frac{6}{7} \Rightarrow \frac{\times}{\times} = \frac{\ }{35}$ **h** $\frac{1}{10} \Rightarrow \frac{\times}{\times} = \frac{\ }{40}$

2 Copy and complete each of these statements.

a $\frac{1}{4} = \frac{2}{8} = \frac{\ }{12} = \frac{4}{\ } = \frac{\ }{20} = \frac{6}{24}$ **b** $\frac{2}{3} = \frac{4}{6} = \frac{\ }{\ } = \frac{\ }{12} = \frac{10}{\ } = \frac{12}{18}$

c $\frac{4}{5} = \frac{\ }{10} = \frac{12}{\ } = \frac{\ }{20} = \frac{\ }{\ } = \frac{\ }{30}$ **d** $\frac{3}{10} = \frac{\ }{\ } = \frac{\ }{30} = \frac{\ }{\ } = \frac{\ }{50} = \frac{18}{\ }$

3 Copy and complete each of these statements.

a $\frac{6}{8} = \frac{6 \div 2}{8 \div 2} = \frac{\ }{\ }$ **b** $\frac{9}{12} = \frac{9 \div 3}{12 \div 3} = \frac{\ }{\ }$

c $\frac{15}{25} = \frac{15 \div 5}{25 \div} = \frac{\ }{\ }$ **d** $\frac{20}{70} = \frac{20 \div 10}{70 \div} = \frac{\ }{\ }$

4 A woman uses her garage to store different items.
She divides the area up into four equal sections.
In one section she put all her items for recycling. In two other sections she stores wine.
The fourth section is empty.

a What fraction of the garage has wine in it?
Give your answer in its simplest form.

b What fraction of the garage is not empty?

5 Cancel each of these fractions to its simplest form.

a $\frac{4}{10}$ **b** $\frac{3}{12}$ **c** $\frac{5}{25}$ **d** $\frac{6}{15}$ **e** $\frac{8}{12}$

f $\frac{10}{30}$ **g** $\frac{12}{20}$ **h** $\frac{16}{24}$ **i** $\frac{30}{50}$ **j** $\frac{42}{49}$

6 Put the following fractions in order with the **smallest** first.

a $\frac{1}{3}, \frac{1}{2}, \frac{1}{4}$ **b** $\frac{3}{4}, \frac{3}{8}, \frac{1}{2}$ **c** $\frac{5}{6}, \frac{2}{3}, \frac{7}{12}$ **d** $\frac{2}{5}, \frac{3}{10}, \frac{1}{4}$

G

F

F

AU 7 Here are four unit fractions.

$\frac{1}{2}$ $\frac{1}{3}$ $\frac{1}{4}$ $\frac{1}{5}$

a Which two of these fractions have a sum of $\frac{5}{6}$?
Show clearly how you work out your answer.

b Which fraction is the smallest?
Explain your answer.

2.5 Improper fractions and mixed numbers

HOMEWORK 2E

F

1 Change each of these top-heavy fractions into a mixed number.

a $\frac{5}{2}$ **b** $\frac{5}{3}$ **c** $\frac{7}{4}$ **d** $\frac{11}{3}$ **e** $\frac{9}{2}$ **f** $\frac{13}{4}$
g $\frac{11}{5}$ **h** $\frac{10}{4}$ **i** $\frac{14}{6}$ **j** $\frac{17}{8}$ **k** $\frac{17}{10}$ **l** $\frac{26}{8}$
m $\frac{12}{4}$ **n** $\frac{20}{5}$ **o** $\frac{60}{10}$

2 Change each of these mixed numbers into a top-heavy fraction.

a $1\frac{1}{2}$ **b** $2\frac{1}{4}$ **c** $2\frac{1}{3}$ **d** $4\frac{1}{2}$ **e** $3\frac{2}{3}$ **f** $1\frac{3}{4}$
g $2\frac{1}{5}$ **h** $2\frac{3}{8}$ **i** $3\frac{2}{5}$ **j** $4\frac{3}{5}$ **k** $5\frac{3}{8}$ **l** $4\frac{3}{7}$
m $5\frac{4}{9}$ **n** $4\frac{5}{12}$ **o** $7\frac{7}{10}$

3 Check your answers to Questions **1** and **2** using the fraction buttons on your calculator.

AU **4** Which of these improper fractions is the biggest?

$\frac{7}{2}$ $\frac{10}{3}$ $\frac{17}{5}$

Show working to justify your answer.

PS **5** Find a mixed number that is greater than $\frac{59}{8}$ and less than $\frac{53}{7}$.

PS **6** Here is a list of numbers.

2 5 9 19

Using one of these numbers for the numerator and one for the denominator, find an improper fraction with a value between 1 and 2.

2.6 Adding and subtracting fractions with the same denominator

HOMEWORK 2F

Example 1 $\frac{5}{9} + \frac{7}{9} = \frac{10}{9} = \frac{4}{3} = 1\frac{1}{3}$ (Cancel down and change to a mixed number.)

Example 2 $\frac{2}{3} + \frac{1}{5} = \frac{10}{15} + \frac{3}{15} = \frac{13}{15}$ (Use equivalent fractions to make the denominators the same.)

F

1 Copy and complete each of these additions.

a $\frac{2}{7} + \frac{4}{7}$ **b** $\frac{4}{9} + \frac{1}{9}$ **c** $\frac{2}{5} + \frac{2}{5}$ **d** $\frac{2}{11} + \frac{3}{11}$ **e** $\frac{3}{13} + \frac{4}{13}$

2 Copy and complete each of these subtractions.

a $\frac{3}{7} - \frac{2}{7}$ **b** $\frac{7}{9} - \frac{2}{9}$ **c** $\frac{7}{11} - \frac{2}{11}$ **d** $\frac{8}{13} - \frac{2}{13}$ **e** $\frac{4}{5} - \frac{1}{5}$

3 Calculate each of these additions. Remember to cancel down.

a $\frac{3}{8} + \frac{1}{8}$ **b** $\frac{3}{10} + \frac{5}{10}$ **c** $\frac{5}{12} + \frac{1}{12}$ **d** $\frac{1}{9} + \frac{5}{9}$ **e** $\frac{2}{15} + \frac{7}{15}$

4 Copy and complete each of these subtractions. Remember to cancel down.

a $\frac{5}{8} - \frac{4}{8}$ **b** $\frac{9}{10} - \frac{3}{10}$ **c** $\frac{5}{9} - \frac{2}{9}$ **d** $\frac{9}{10} - \frac{3}{10}$ **e** $\frac{7}{8} - \frac{1}{8}$

5 Calculate each of these additions. Remember to use equivalent fractions.

a $\frac{1}{3}+\frac{1}{2}$ **b** $\frac{2}{5}+\frac{3}{10}$ **c** $\frac{1}{4}+\frac{5}{12}$ **d** $\frac{3}{5}+\frac{1}{4}$ **e** $\frac{3}{4}+\frac{2}{3}$

6 Calculate each of these subtractions.

a $\frac{5}{8}-\frac{1}{8}$ **b** $\frac{7}{10}-\frac{3}{10}$ **c** $\frac{11}{12}-\frac{3}{4}$ **d** $\frac{2}{3}-\frac{1}{2}$ **e** $\frac{9}{10}-\frac{1}{5}$

7 At a cricket match, $\frac{9}{10}$ of the crowd were men. What fraction of the crowd were women?

8 An iceberg shows $\frac{1}{9}$ of its mass above sea level. What fraction of it is below sea level?

9 A petrol gauge shows that a tank is $\frac{7}{12}$ full. What fraction of the tank is empty?

FM 10 David spends $\frac{1}{4}$ of his pocket money on bus fares, $\frac{1}{3}$ on magazines and saves the rest. He wants to save half of his pocket money. Does he succeed?

11 In a local election Mr Weeks received $\frac{2}{5}$ of the total votes, Ms Meenan received $\frac{1}{4}$ and Mr White received the remainder. What fraction of the total votes did Mr White receive?

AU 12 On a certain day at a busy railway station, $\frac{7}{10}$ of the trains arriving were on time, $\frac{1}{6}$ were late by 10 minutes or less and the rest were late by more than 10 minutes. What fraction of the trains arrived late by more than 10 minutes?

2.7 Finding a fraction of a quantity

HOMEWORK 2G

1 Calculate each of these.

a $\frac{1}{2}$ of 20 **b** $\frac{1}{3}$ of 36 **c** $\frac{1}{4}$ of 24

d $\frac{3}{4}$ of 40 **e** $\frac{2}{3}$ of 15 **f** $\frac{1}{5}$ of 30

g $\frac{3}{8}$ of 16 **h** $\frac{7}{10}$ of 50

2 Calculate each of these quantities.

a $\frac{1}{4}$ of £800 **b** $\frac{2}{3}$ of 60 kilograms **c** $\frac{3}{4}$ of 200 metres

d $\frac{3}{8}$ of 48 gallons **e** $\frac{4}{5}$ of 30 minutes **f** $\frac{7}{10}$ of 120 miles

3 In each case, find out which is the smaller number.

a $\frac{1}{4}$ of 60 or $\frac{1}{2}$ of 40 **b** $\frac{1}{3}$ of 36 or $\frac{1}{5}$ of 50

c $\frac{2}{3}$ of 15 or $\frac{3}{4}$ of 12 **d** $\frac{5}{8}$ of 72 or $\frac{5}{6}$ of 60

4 $\frac{5}{9}$ of a class of 36 students are girls. How many boys are there in the class?

FM 5 Mrs Wilson puts $\frac{3}{20}$ of her weekly wage into a pension scheme. How much does she put into the scheme if her wage one week is £320?

6 Mitchell spent one third of a day sleeping and one quarter at school. How many hours are left for doing other things?

7 A bush is 40 cm tall when planted in spring. Its height increases by $\frac{3}{10}$ during the summer.

a Find $\frac{3}{10}$ of 40 cm.

b Find the height of the bush at the end of the summer.

FM 8 A travel agent has this sign in its window. Marion books a holiday for her family which would normally cost £800.

a How much does she save?

b How much does she pay for the holiday after the reduction?

⅕ OFF
all holiday prices for next year if booked before December

E

PS 9 A chair is advertised at Top Sofa for £800, including a free footstool, but with an offer of one-quarter off.
The same chair is advertised at Comfy Seats for £480 and the footstool costs £130 extra.
Which shop is cheaper for buying both the chair and the footstool?

2.8 Multiplying and dividing fractions

HOMEWORK 2H

E

1 Work out each of these multiplications.

a $\frac{1}{2} \times \frac{1}{2}$	**b** $\frac{1}{3} \times \frac{1}{5}$	**c** $\frac{1}{4} \times \frac{1}{3}$
d $\frac{3}{4} \times \frac{1}{2}$	**e** $\frac{1}{3} \times \frac{3}{5}$	**f** $\frac{2}{3} \times \frac{1}{2}$
g $\frac{4}{5} \times \frac{1}{2}$	**h** $\frac{5}{6} \times \frac{1}{5}$	**i** $\frac{3}{8} \times \frac{2}{3}$
j $\frac{3}{10} \times \frac{5}{6}$		

FM PS 2 A printer is cutting sheets of paper down to smaller sizes.
He cuts each sheet into quarters and then cuts each quarter in half.

a What fraction of the original sheet is each new sheet?

b Each small sheet is sold for 10p. How many large sheets should be cut up to make £20?

D

AU 3 There are 270 000 people living in Rotherham. One-sixth of these are aged over 60. Of the over-60s, two-thirds are women.

a What fraction of the whole population are women over 60?

b How many woman over 60 live in Rotherham?

2.9 One quantity as a fraction of another

HOMEWORK 2I

Example Write £5 as a fraction of £20.

$\frac{5}{20} = \frac{1}{4}$ (Cancel down)

D

1 Write the first quantity as a fraction of the second.

a £2, £8	**b** 9 cm, 12 cm	**c** 18 miles, 30 miles
d 200 g, 350 g	**e** 20 seconds, 1 minute	**f** 25p, £2

2 During a one-hour TV programme, 10 minutes were devoted to adverts. What fraction of the time was given to adverts?

AU 3 On an 80-mile car journey, 50 miles were driven on a motorway. What fraction of the journey was not driven on a motorway?

4 In a class, 24 students were right-handed and 6 students were left-handed.
What fraction of the class were:

a right-handed **b** left-handed?

FM 5 Mark earns £120 and saves £40 of it.
Bev earns £150 and saves £60 of it.
Who is saving the greater proportion of their earnings?

D

FM 6 In a test, Kevin scores 7 out of 10 and Sally scores 15 out of 20. Which is the better mark?
Explain your answer.

Functional Maths Activity

Organising the school timetable

In a school there are **180** students in year 10 and you want to organise them in to classes for different option subjects.
The Heads of Department give you the following facts:

Languages (Spanish and French)
All students take one language, except for one group of 26 students who go out on a work placement.

Spanish
Half of all students do Spanish.
They are all taught at the same time.
There are three equal-sized classes.

French
There are three classes.
The smallest class has one-quarter of the students taking French.
The other two classes have the same number of students in each.

Geography
Two-thirds of all students in the year group take geography.
There are five equal-sized classes.

History
Two-fifths of all students take history.
One class has 21 students and one class has 18 students.
There are two other classes. Two-thirds of the remaining students are in one class.

Copy and complete the table for the classes. Remember that there are 180 students in the year group.
Choose your own rules for PE.
Decide the number of classes and work out the number in each class so that no PE class exceeds 30 students.

Subject	Number in each class			
Spanish				
French				
Geography				
History				
PE				

Functional Maths Activity (continued)

Now copy and complete this table to give the fraction of the year group in each class.

Subject	**Fraction of whole year group in each class**			
Spanish				
French				
Geography				
History				
PE				

3 Number: Negative numbers

3.1 Introduction to negative numbers

HOMEWORK 3A

1 Write down the temperatures for each thermometer.

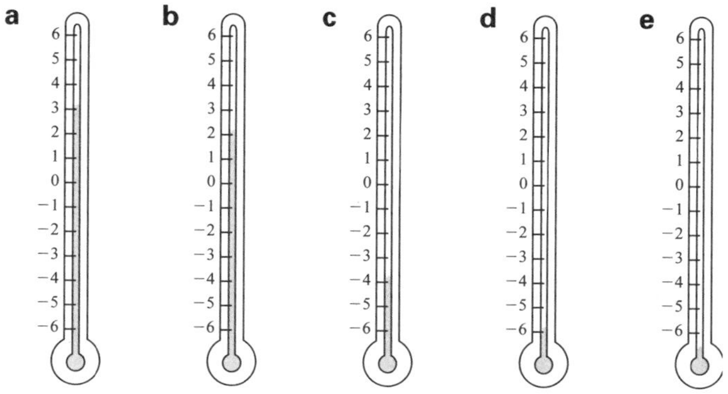

2 Look at this map showing average temperatures in the capital cities of England, Scotland and Wales.

a How much colder is it in Edinburgh than Cardiff?

b How much warmer is it in Cardiff than Edinburgh?

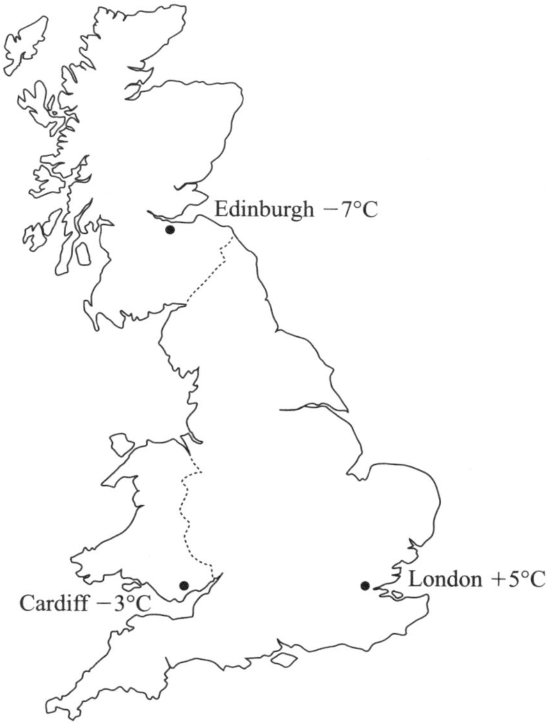

G

AU PS **3** The diagram shows the layout of a hotel and the lift numbers for each floor.

a How many floors is the third floor above the basement?

b How many floors is the lower ground floor below the first floor?

c How many floors is the basement below the second floor?

d The cellar basement is three floors below the basement. What number is used for the lift?

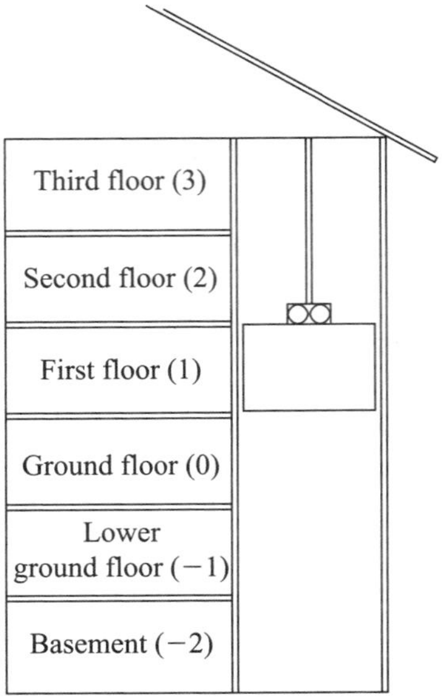

3.2 Everyday use of negative numbers

HOMEWORK 3B

G

Copy and complete each of the following.

1 If +£20 means a profit of twenty pounds, then .... means a loss of twenty pounds.

2 If –£10 means a loss of ten pounds, then +£10 means a .... of ten pounds.

3 If +500 m means 500 metres above sea level, then .... means 500 metres below sea level.

4 If –1000 m means one thousand metres below sea level, then +1000 m means one thousand metres .... sea level.

5 If +7°C means seven degrees above freezing point, then .... means seven degrees below freezing point.

6 If +1°C means 1°C above freezing point, then .... means 1°C below freezing point.

7 If –15°C means fifteen degrees below freezing point, then +15°C means fifteen degrees .... freezing point.

8 If –5000 miles means five thousand miles south of the equator, then +5000 miles means five thousand miles .... of the equator.

9 If a car moving forwards at 25 mph is represented by +25 mph, then a car moving backwards at 10 mph is represented by ....

10 In multi-storey car park, the sixth floor above ground level is represented by +6. So, the third floor below ground level is represented by ....

PS **11** A hotel has 11 levels numbered from basement (–1) to ninth floor (+9).
A man is in a lift on the third floor. He goes up four levels and then down to the basement.
How many levels does the lift travel while descending?

FM 12 Here is Faisal's bank statement.

Sproggit & Sylvester Bank

Customer ID: 5436t499
Statement no: 4565
Statement date: 29 SEP 2009

Date	Description	Debits	Credits	Balance
21 Sept 2009	Electricity bill 125.48...	£125.32	...	£250.80
24 Sept 2009	Cheque	...	£30.00	£155.48
29 Sept 2009	Water bill	£162.50	...	−£7.02

a How much does he owe the bank?

b On 30th September he pays in £10.
How much has he in the bank now?

AU 13 The temperature on three days in Quebec in Canada was −9°C, −8°C and −11°C.

a Put the temperatures in order starting with the coldest.

b What is the difference in temperature between the coldest and the warmest temperature?

3.3 The number line

HOMEWORK 3C

Use the number line to answer Questions **1** and **2**.

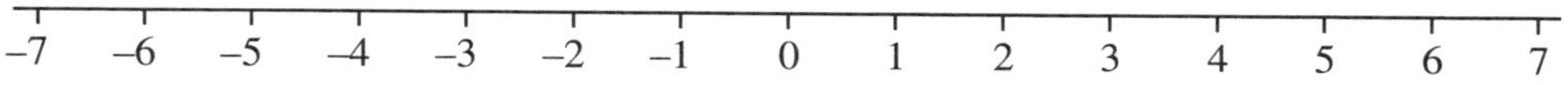

1 Complete each of the following by putting a suitable number in the box.

a ☐ is smaller than 6 **b** ☐ is smaller than 2
c ☐ is smaller than −1 **d** ☐ is smaller than −6
e −4 is smaller than ☐ **f** −7 is smaller than ☐
g 5 is smaller than ☐ **h** 4 is smaller than ☐
i ☐ is smaller than 0 **j** −1 is smaller than ☐

2 Complete each of the following by putting a suitable number in the box.

a ☐ is bigger than −6 **b** ☐ is bigger than 4
c ☐ is bigger than −2 **d** ☐ is bigger than 0
e −3 is bigger than ☐ **f** −5 is bigger than ☐
g 1 is bigger than ☐ **h** −1 is bigger than ☐
i ☐ is bigger than −4 **j** 3 is bigger than ☐

3 In each case below, put the correct symbol, either < or >, in the box.

a 2 ☐ 6 **b** −1 ☐ −7
c −5 ☐ 1 **d** 5 ☐ 9
e −8 ☐ 2 **f** −14 ☐ −10
g −11 ☐ 0 **h** −9 ☐ −12
i 8 ☐ −3 **j** 0 ☐ −8

HINTS AND TIPS

Reminder: The inequality signs: < means 'is less than' and > means 'is greater than'.

G

PS 4 Copy these number lines and fill in the missing numbers on each line.

a
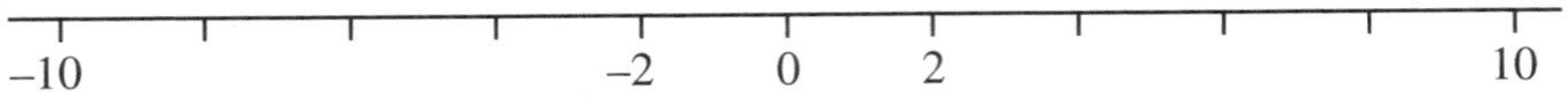

b
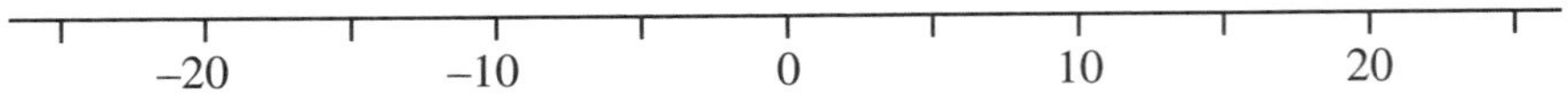

c
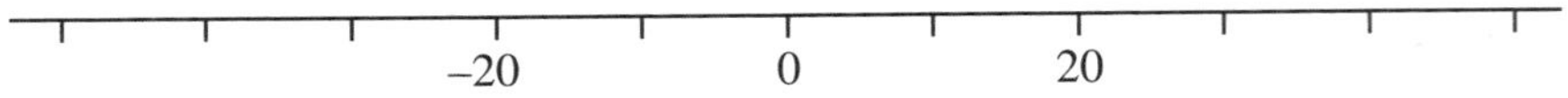

d
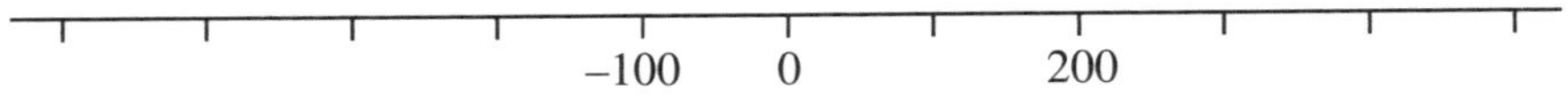

e
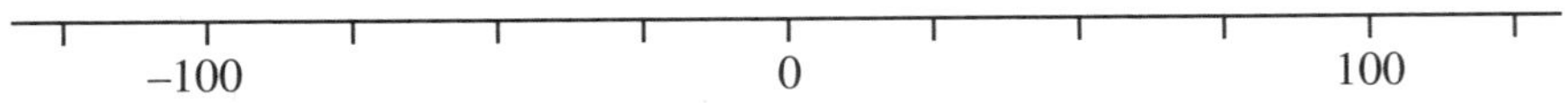

FM 5 Here are some temperatures.

3°C –8°C –1°C 4°C

Copy and complete the following weather report using these temperatures.

Temperatures fell to ...., making Newcastle the coldest place in the country today, while in Yorkshire the temperatures were also below freezing at .... People on the south coast enjoyed warmer temperatures, with Eastbourne being the warmest at .... and Brighton only slightly lower at ....

AU 6 Here are some numbers.

$-2\frac{3}{4}$ $+1\frac{1}{2}$ $-1\frac{1}{4}$

Copy the number line below and mark the numbers on it.

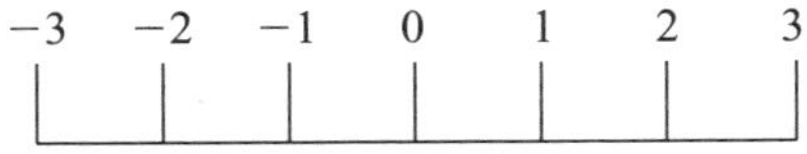

3.4 Arithmetic with negative numbers

HOMEWORK 3D

Example 1 –3 + 5 = 2

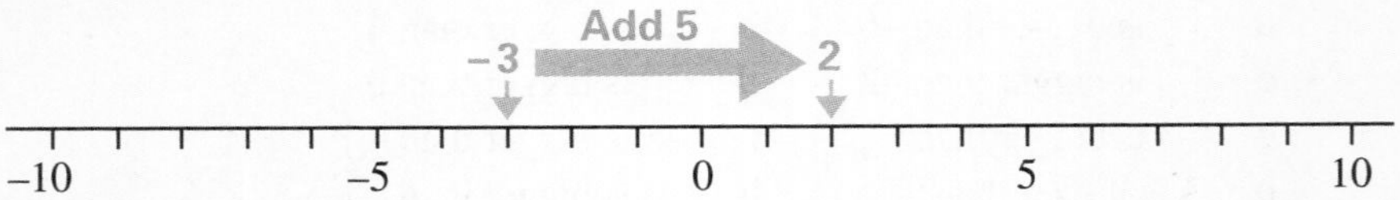

Example 2 –4 – 5 = –9

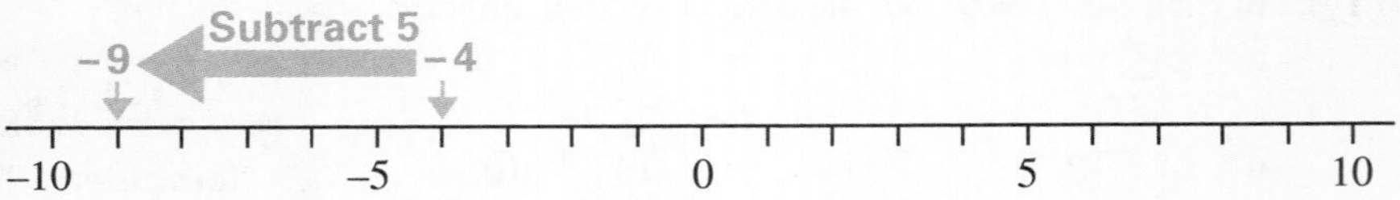

F

1 Use the number line to find the answer to each of the following.

a $-2 + 5 =$	**b** $-4 + 6 =$	**c** $-3 + 4 =$	**d** $-1 + 5 =$
e $-6 + 8 =$	**f** $-5 + 10 =$	**g** $-2 + 2 =$	**h** $-4 + 4 =$
i $4 - 5 =$	**j** $6 - 8 =$	**k** $3 - 7 =$	**l** $5 - 9 =$
m $-5 + 3 =$	**n** $-2 + 1 =$	**o** $-10 + 6 =$	**p** $-8 + 6 =$
q $-2 - 7 =$	**r** $-1 - 5 =$	**s** $-3 - 7 =$	**t** $-5 - 5 =$

2 Answer each of the following without the help of the number scale.

a $15 - 19 =$	**b** $3 - 17 =$	**c** $-2 - 10 =$	**d** $-12 + 7 =$
e $-15 + 9 =$	**f** $10 - 20 =$	**g** $-10 - 12 =$	**h** $-15 - 20 =$
i $23 - 30 =$			

3 Work out each of the following.

a $1 + 3 - 5 =$	**b** $-4 + 8 - 2 =$	**c** $-6 + 3 - 4 =$	**d** $-3 - 5 + 4 =$
e $-1 - 1 + 5 =$	**f** $-7 + 5 + 8 =$	**g** $-3 - 4 + 7 =$	**h** $1 - 3 - 6 =$
i $-5 - 3 - 2 =$			

4 Check your answers to questions 1 to 3 using a calculator.

AU 5 At noon the temperature in Glasgow was –3°C.
At 2 pm the temperature had risen by 2°C.

a What is the temperature at 2 pm?

b At 6 pm the temperature was 5 degrees lower than it was at 2 pm. What was the temperature at 6 pm?

PS 6 Here are five numbers.

5 9 1 3 4

a Use two of the numbers to make a calculation with an answer of –5.

b Use three of the numbers to make a calculation with an answer of –11.

c Use four of the numbers to make a calculation with an answer of –10.

d Use all five of the numbers to make a calculation with an answer of –20.

HOMEWORK 3E

Example 1 $4 - (-2) = 4 + 2 = 6$

Example 2 $3 + (-5) = 3 - 5 = -2$

F

1 Answer each of the following. Check your answers on a calculator.

a $2 + (-5) =$	**b** $6 - (-3) =$	**c** $3 + (-5) =$	**d** $8 - (-2) =$
e $-6 + (-2) =$	**f** $-5 + (-2) =$	**g** $-2 - (-5) =$	**h** $-7 - (-1) =$
i $-2 - (-2) =$			

2 Write down the answer to each of the following, then check your answers on a calculator.

a $-13 - 5 =$	**b** $-12 - 8 =$	**c** $-25 + 6 =$	**d** $6 - 14 =$
e $25 - -3 =$	**f** $13 - -8 =$	**g** $-4 + -15 =$	**h** $-13 + -7 =$
i $-12 + -9 =$	**j** $-16 + -12 =$		

3 The temperature at midday was 5°C. Find the temperature at midnight if it fell by:

a 1°C **b** 5°C **c** 6°C **d** 8°C **e** 12°C.

F

4 What is the difference between the following temperatures?

a 4°C and 6°C **b** –2°C and 4°C **c** –3°C and –6°C

5 Rewrite the following lists, putting the numbers in order of size, smallest first.

a 2 –5 3 –6 –3 8 –1 1

b 4 –8 5 –10 –5 0 6 –12

AU 6 Write down five addition and five subtraction calculations that give an answer of –5.

AU 7 You have the following cards.

5	3	2	–1	–3	–6

a Which other card should you choose to make the answer to the following sum as large as possible? What is the answer?

5 + ☐ = ☐

b Which other card should you choose to make the answer to part **a** as small as possible? What is the answer?

c Which other card should you choose to make the answer to the following sum as large as possible? What is the answer?

5 – ☐ = ☐

d Which other card should you choose to make the answer to part **c** as small as possible? What is the answer?

e Which two cards should you choose to make the answer to an addition sum zero?

8 Two numbers have a sum of 8. One of the numbers is negative. The other number is odd. What could the numbers be? Give two different answers

HOMEWORK 3F

F

1 Find the next three numbers in each sequence.

a 6, 4, 2, 0, …, …, …

b 8, 5, 2, –1, …, …, …

c –20, –15, –10, –5, …, …, …

d 10, 9, 7, 4, …, …, …

e –12, $-10\frac{1}{2}$, –9, $-7\frac{1}{2}$, …, …, …

FM 2 The deep freeze compartment in a refrigerator should be set at –14°C, but in error is set to –6°C. How does the temperature setting need to be changed so that it is correct?

FM 3 At 5am, the temperature on a thermometer outside Brian's house was –4°C. By midday, the temperature had risen by 10°C.

a What was the temperature at midday?

By midnight, the temperature had fallen to –9°C.

b What was the fall in temperature from midday to midnight?

4 The table shows the recorded highest and lowest temperatures in five cities during one year.

	London	New York	Athens	Beijing	Nairobi
Highest temperature (°C)	30	28	36	31	29
Lowest temperature (°C)	–5	–8	5	–10	11

a Which city had the highest temperature?

b Which city had the largest difference in temperature and by how many degrees?

c Which city had the smallest difference in temperature and by how many degrees?

5 This is a two-step function machine. Use the function machine to complete the table.

Number in ➡ **Add 2** ➡ **Subtract 5** ➡ **Number out**

Number in	Number out
10	
2	
–1	
	0
	–8

PS 6 Copy and complete this magic square. Write down the magic number.

1	–6	–1
–4		

F

Functional Maths Activity

The hotel lift

In a hotel, there are seven floors and one lift, as shown in the diagram opposite.
The manager of the hotel works out that the average time for a lift to move from one floor to the next is 15 seconds.
Reception is on the ground floor.
Bedrooms are on the first to fourth floors.
The gymnasium is in the lower basement.
Guests have complained that the lifts take too long to arrive.

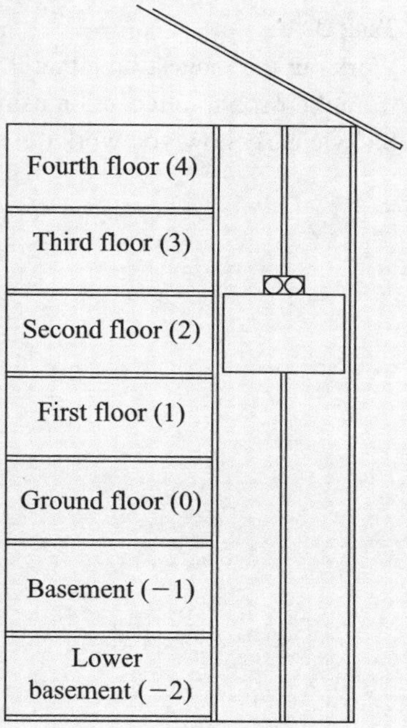

Task 1
Complete the table to work out the number of floors the lift has to travel (– for down and + for up).
The first few have been done for you.

		From						
		–2	**–1**	**0**	**1**	**2**	**3**	**4**
To	**–2**	———	–1					
	–1	+1	———					
	0			———				
	1				———			
	2					———		
	3						———	
	4							———

Functional Maths Activity (continued)

Task 2

The manager works out that the average time for a lift to move from one floor to the next is actually 15 seconds when going down and 20 seconds when going up.

Complete this table to show the times for the lift to move between floors.

		From						
		–2	**–1**	**0**	**1**	**2**	**3**	**4**
To	**–2**	———	15 sec					
	–1	20 sec	———					
	0			———				
	1				———			
	2					———		
	3						———	
	4							———

Task 3

Work out the longest time that it would take someone to get from their room to reception using the lift.

Show clearly how you work out your answer.

HINTS AND TIPS

The answer is not 60 seconds.

4 Number: Number properties 1

4.1 Multiples of whole numbers

HOMEWORK 4A

1 Write out the first five multiples of:
a 4 **b** 6 **c** 8 **d** 12 **e** 15.
Remember: the first multiple is the number itself.

2 From the list of numbers below
28 19 36 43 64 53 77 66 56 60 15 29 61 45 51
write down those that are:
a multiples of 4 **b** multiples of 5 **c** multiples of 8 **d** multiples of 11.

3 Use your calculator to see which of the numbers below are:
a multiples of 7 **b** multiples of 9 **c** multiples of 12.
225 252 361 297 162 363 161 289 224 205 312 378 315 182 369

PS **4** Find the biggest number smaller than 200 that is:
a a multiple of 2 **b** a multiple of 4 **c** a multiple of 5 **d** a multiple of 8
e a multiple of 9.

PS **5** Find the smallest number that is a multiple of 3 and bigger than:
a 10 **b** 100 **c** 1000 **d** 10 000 **e** 1 000 000 000.

6 There are 12 sweets in a bag. There are 96 sweets ready to put into bags.
Will all the bags be full?
Give a reason for your answer.

7 48 people are at a wedding reception. The tables are arranged so that the same number of people sit at each table.
How many people sit at each table?
Give **two** possible answers.

8 Here is a list of numbers.
4 9 10 12 14 20
a From the list, write down a multiple of 7.
b From the list, write down a multiple of 6.
c From the list, write down a multiple of both 4 and 5.

PS **9** Find the lowest odd number that is a multiple of 9 and a multiple of 15.

4.2 Factors of whole numbers

HOMEWORK 4B

Example Find the factors of 32.

Look for the pairs of numbers which make 32 when multiplied together. These are

$1 \times 32 = 32$, $2 \times 16 = 32$ and $4 \times 8 = 32$. So the factors of 32 are 1, 2, 4, 8, 16, 32.

G

1 What are the factors of each of these numbers?

a 12 **b** 13 **c** 15 **d** 20 **e** 22
f 36 **g** 42 **h** 48 **i** 49 **j** 50

2 Use your calculator to find the factors of each of these numbers.

a 100 **b** 111 **c** 125 **d** 132 **e** 140

PS **3** All the numbers in **a** to **j** are divisible by 11. Use your calculator to divide each one by 11 and then write down the answer. What do you notice?

a 143 **b** 253 **c** 275 **d** 363 **e** 462
f 484 **g** 561 **h** 583 **i** 792 **j** 891

FM **4** Fred wants to pack 18 items into boxes so that there are exactly the same number of items in each box. How many ways can he do this?

5 Here is a list of numbers.

3 6 8 10 13

a From the list, write down a factor of 32.
b From the list, write down a factor of 20.
c From the list, write down a factor of both 26 and 39.

AU **6** Here are five numbers

15 20 24 27 30

Use factors to explain why 20 could be the odd one out.

F

PS **7** Find the highest even number that is a factor of 30 and a factor of 42.

4.3 Prime numbers

HOMEWORK 4C

E

1 Write down all the prime numbers less than 40.

2 Which of these numbers are prime?

43 47 49 51 54 57 59 61 65 67

3 This is a number pattern to generate odd numbers.

Line 1 $2 - 1 = 1$
Line 2 $2 \times 2 - 1 = 3$
Line 3 $2 \times 2 \times 2 - 1 = 7$

a Work out the next three lines of the pattern.
b Which lines have answers that are prime numbers?

PS **4** Using the rules for recognising multiples, decide which of these numbers are not prime.

39 41 51 71 123

AU **5** When two different prime numbers are multiplied together the answer is 91.
What are the two prime numbers?

6 **a** Write down two prime numbers with a difference of 6.
b Write down two more prime numbers with a difference of 6.

FM **7** A mechanic has a set of 23 spanners.
Is it possible to put them in a toolbox so that he has the same number of spanners in each part of his box?
Explain your answer.

4.4 Square numbers

HOMEWORK 4D

1 Write down the first ten square numbers.

PS 2 Here is a number pattern.

$2 \times 0 + 1 = 1$
$3 \times 1 + 1 = 4$
$4 \times 2 + 1 = 9$

a Write down the next three lines in the pattern.
b Describe what you notice about the answers to each line of the pattern.

3 Write down the answer to each of the following. You will need to use your calculator.

a 5^2 **b** 15^2 **c** 25^2 **d** 35^2 **e** 45^2
f 55^2 **g** 65^2 **h** 75^2 **i** 85^2 **j** 95^2

Describe any pattern you notice.

4 **a** Write down the value of 11^2.
b Estimate the value of 10.5^2.

5 How much do 15 rulers at 15 pence each cost?

6 A builder buys 60 bricks for 60 pence each.
She has £40. How many extra bricks can she afford to buy?

7 In a warehouse, books are stored on shelves in piles of 20.
How many books are on two shelves, if there are ten piles of books on each shelf?

HOMEWORK 4E

1 Write down the first five multiples of:

a 5 **b** 7 **c** 16 **d** 25 **e** 30.

Remember: the first multiple is the number itself.

2 Write down all the factors of each of these numbers.

a 18 **b** 25 **c** 28 **d** 35 **e** 40

3 Write down the first three numbers that are multiples of both:

a 2 and 5 **b** 3 and 4 **c** 5 and 6 **d** 4 and 6 **e** 8 and 10.

4 In a prize draw, raffle tickets are numbered from 1 to 100.
A prize is given if a ticket drawn is a multiple of 10 or a multiple of 15.
Which ticket holders will receive two prizes?

AU 5 Here is a number pattern using square numbers.

$1^2 - 0^2 = 1$
$2^2 - 1^2 = 3$
$3^2 - 2^2 = 5$
$4^2 - 3^2 = 7$

a Write down the next three lines in the pattern.
b What do you think is the answer to $21^2 - 20^2$?
Explain your answer.

F

6 From the list of numbers below:

4 6 7 10 13 16 21 23 25 28 34 37 40 49 50

write down those that are:

a prime numbers;

b square numbers.

E

AU 7 Here are four numbers.

3 12 25 36

Copy and complete the table by putting the numbers in the correct boxes.

	Square number	**Factor of 24**
Odd number		
Multiple of 6		

AU 8 Use these four number cards to make a square number.

0 1 2 4

4.5 Square roots

HOMEWORK 4F

F

1 Write down the positive square root of each of these numbers.

a 64 **b** 25 **c** 49 **d** 81 **e** 16
f 36 **g** 100 **h** 121 **i** 144 **j** 400

2 Write down the answer to each of the following. You will need to use your calculator.

a $\sqrt{225}$ **b** $\sqrt{289}$ **c** $\sqrt{441}$ **d** $\sqrt{625}$ **e** $\sqrt{1089}$
f $\sqrt{1369}$ **g** $\sqrt{3136}$ **h** $\sqrt{6084}$ **i** $\sqrt{40\,804}$ **j** $\sqrt{110\,889}$

PS 3 Here is a number pattern using square roots and square numbers.

$$\sqrt{1} = 1$$
$$\sqrt{1} + \sqrt{4} = 3$$
$$\sqrt{1} + \sqrt{4} + \sqrt{9} = 6$$

a Write down the next three lines in the pattern.

b Describe any pattern you notice in the answers.

AU 4 Put these in order starting with the smallest value.

2^2 $\sqrt{20}$ $\sqrt{10}$ 3^2

AU 5 Between which two consecutive whole numbers does the square root of 40 lie?

E

PS 6 A child has 125 square tiles which she is arranging into square patterns.
How many tiles will be in the biggest square she can make?

FM 7 Square floor tiles are being fitted on a square kitchen floor.
Altogether it needs 121 tiles.
How many tiles are needed for each row?

4.6 Powers

HOMEWORK 4G

Example Work out 3^5.

$3^5 = 3 \times 3 \times 3 \times 3 \times 3 = 243$

1 Use your calculator to work out the value of each of the following.

a 2^3 **b** 4^3 **c** 7^3 **d** 10^3 **e** 12^3
f 3^4 **g** 10^4 **h** 2^5 **i** 10^6 **j** 2^8

PS 2 Use your calculator to work out the answers to the following powers of 11.

a 11^2 **b** 11^3 **c** 11^4

Describe any patterns you notice in your answers.

Does your pattern work for other powers of 11? Give a reason for your answer.

3

1	2	3	4	5	6	7	8	9
10	11	12	13	14	15	16	17	18
19	20	21	22	23	24	25	26	27
28	29	30	31	32	33	34	35	36

From the numbers above, write down:

a all the multiples of 7
b all the factors of 30
c all the prime numbers
d the square of 6
e the square root of 25
f the cube of 3.

4 A box is in the shape of a cube.

The height of the box is 30 centimetres.

To work out the volume of a cube, use the formula

Volume = $(\text{length of edge})^3$

Work out the volume of the box.

AU 5 Write each number as a power of a different number.

The first one has been done for you.

a $16 = 2^4$
b $64 =$
c $27 =$
d $36 =$

E

D

Problem-solving Activity

The alternative square root

My square root button has broken.

How can I find a square root using the other buttons?
Here is a method for calculating square roots without using a square root button.

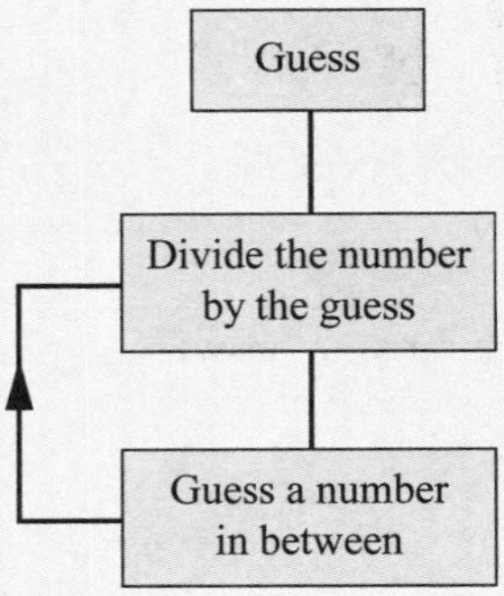

Example $\sqrt{60}$

Guess 7

$60 \div 7 = 8.5$

New guess 8

$60 \div 8 = 7.5$

New guess 7.8

$60 \div 7.8 = 7.692$

New guess 7.75

$60 \div 7.75 = 7.74$

Answer is between 7.74 and 7.75

Exact answer 7.7459

Task 1
Use this method to find $\sqrt{1000}$ and then $\sqrt{130}$.
In each case give your answer to 1 decimal place.
Check your answers using the square root button.

Task 2
Choose your own number and use this method to find its square root.

5 Statistics: Statistical representation

5.1 Frequency diagrams

HOMEWORK 5A

E

1 For the following surveys, decide whether the data should be collected by:
i sampling **ii** observation **iii** experiment.

a The number of 'doubles' obtained when throwing two dice.
b The number of people who use a zebra-crossing on a busy main road.
c People's choice of favourite restaurant.
d The makes of cars parked in the staff car-park.
e The number of times a 'head' appears when throwing a coin.
f The type of food students prefer to eat in the school canteen.

2 In a game, a fair six-sided dice has its faces numbered 0, 1 or 2.
The dice is thrown 36 times and the results are shown below.

2 0 2 2 1 2 0 2 2 0 0 2
1 2 2 2 0 2 2 0 1 2 2 1
0 2 2 0 2 0 2 2 0 1 2 0

a Copy and complete the frequency table for the data.

Number	Tally	Frequency
0		
1		
2		

b Based on the results in the table, how many times do you think each number appears on the dice?

D

3 The table shows the average highest daily temperature recorded during August in 24 cities around the world.

City	Temperature (°C)	City	Temperature (°C)
Athens	33	Madras	35
Auckland	15	Marrakesh	38
Bangkok	32	Moscow	22
Budapest	27	Narvik	16
Buenos Aires	16	Nice	29
Cape Town	18	Oporto	25
Dubai	39	Perth	17
Geneva	25	Pisa	30
Istanbul	28	Quebec	23
La Paz	17	Reykjavik	14
London	20	Tokyo	30
Luxor	41	Tripoli	31

a Copy and complete the grouped frequency table for the data.

Temperature (°C)	Tally	Frequency
11–15		
16–20		
21–25		
26–30		
31–35		
36–40		
41–45		

b In how many cities was the temperature higher than the temperature in London?

c Kay said that the difference between the highest and lowest temperatures was 34°C but Derek said that it is was 27°C. Explain how they obtained different answers.

4 Heather attends a Spanish evening class at her local college. One evening she conducted a survey of the ages of all the people who attended. She wrote down all the ages on a piece of paper as follows.

25 41 33 24 46
37 40 32 59
64 37 26 44
58 31 29 19
37 30 22
48 51 68 28 27
51 34 49

a How many people attended on that evening?

b Copy and complete the grouped frequency table for the data.

Age	Tally	Frequency
11–20		
21–30		
31–40		
41–50		
51–60		
61–70		

c How many people were aged under 21? Suggest a possible reason for this.

5 Pat measured the heights, to the nearest centimetre, of all the students in her class. Her data is given below.

143 135 147 153 146 138 151
142 139 131 144 127 143 145
140 143 153 141 150 137 136
125 136 140 131 147 154 142

a Draw a grouped frequency table for the data using class intervals 125–129, 130–134, 135–139, …

b In which interval do the most heights lie?

c How many students had a height of 140 cm or more?

FM 6 Mr Speed's class did a geology test with 14 questions. The test scores are shown below.

7 9 9 10 12 11 10 11 11 12 12 13 13 13

10 9 9 10 9 9 9 10 8 8 7 8 7 8 7 9

He wanted to assess how well the class had done.

a Create a frequency table showing these results.

b What test score appears the most?

c Describe the class test results.

PS 7 Azam timed how long each patient waited in a hospital's casualty department one evening. The following is his record in minutes.

28 4 31 11 31 6 24 5 36 17 10 29 7 15 20

26 32 19 27 13 24 7 15 32 8 4 38 19 34 12

33 22 34 21 25 9 25 5 18 9 34 13 23 40 8 35 20 29

Find the best way to put this data into a frequency chart to illustrate the length of time that different patients had to wait.

Explain why you chose the time ranges you used.

AU 8 Hannah wants to do a survey on the prices charged for soft drinks in her neighbourhood. She said, 'I will make a frequency table with the regions 1p–40p, 40p–60p and 60p–£1.' Give two reasons why these class divisions may present a problem.

5.2 Statistical diagrams

HOMEWORK 5B

1 The pictogram shows the number of copies of *The Times* sold by a newsagent in a particular week.

		Total
Monday		12
Tuesday		
Wednesday		
Thursday		
Friday		
Saturday		

a How many newspapers does the symbol  represent?

b Complete the totals for Tuesday, Wednesday and Thursday.

c The newsagent sold 15 copies on Friday and 22 copies on Saturday.
Complete the pictogram for Friday and Saturday.

2 The pictogram shows the amount of sunshine in five English holiday resorts on one day in August.

Key:  represents 3 hours.

a Write down the number of hours of sunshine for each resort.

b Great Yarmouth had $5\frac{1}{2}$ hours of sunshine on the same day. Explain why this would be difficult to show on this pictogram.

3 The pictogram shows the number of call-outs five taxi drivers had on one evening.

Key: ✪ represents 10 call-outs.

a How many call-outs did each taxi driver have?

b Explain why the symbol used in this pictogram is not really suitable.

c Joanne had 16 call-outs on the same evening. Redraw a suitable pictogram to show the call-outs for the six taxi drivers.

4 Rachel did a survey to show the number of people in each car on their way to work on a particular morning. This is a copy of her survey sheet.

No. of people in each car	Frequency
1	30
2	19
3	12
4	5
5 or more	1

Draw a pictogram to illustrate her data.

FM 5 A form did a survey to see who received most emails in a week on their school email account.

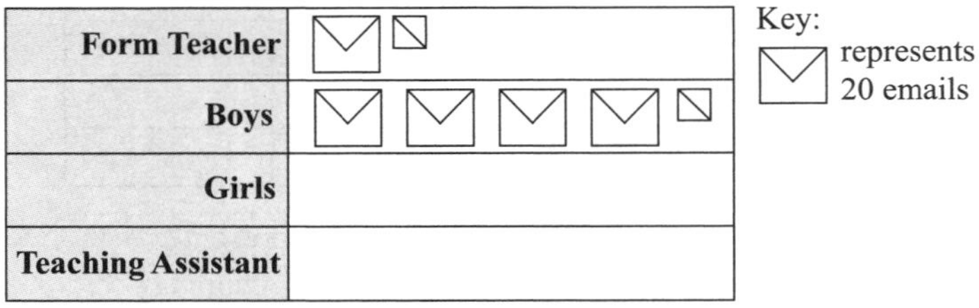

a How many emails did:

i the form teacher receive? **ii** the boys receive?

b Draw that part of the pictogram that will show the 110 girls' emails.

c What problem does the teaching assistant's 13 emails present?

PS 6 A survey was taken on what types of shows the parents of the students had seen at the local theatre in the last six months.

	Frequency
Musicals	128
Comedy	48
Drama	80

This information had to be put into a pictogram.
Design a pictogram to show this information with a sensible number of symbols.

AU **7** A pictogram is to be made from this frequency table.

England	405
Ireland	85
Wales	115
Scotland	325

Explain why a key of five people to a symbol is not a good idea.

5.3 Bar charts

HOMEWORK 5C

1 Linda asked a sample of people 'What is your favourite soap opera?'. The bar chart shows their replies.

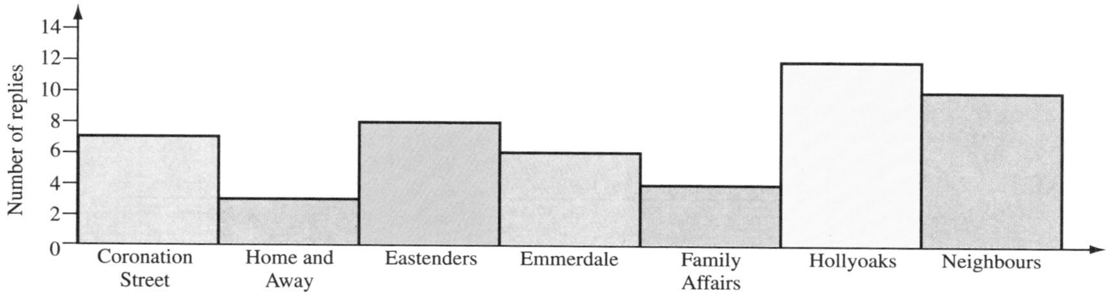

a Which soap opera got six replies?

b How many people were in Linda's sample?

c Linda collected the data from all her friends in Year 10 at school. Give two reasons why this is not a good way to collect the data.

2 The bar chart shows the results of a survey of shoe sizes in form 10KE.

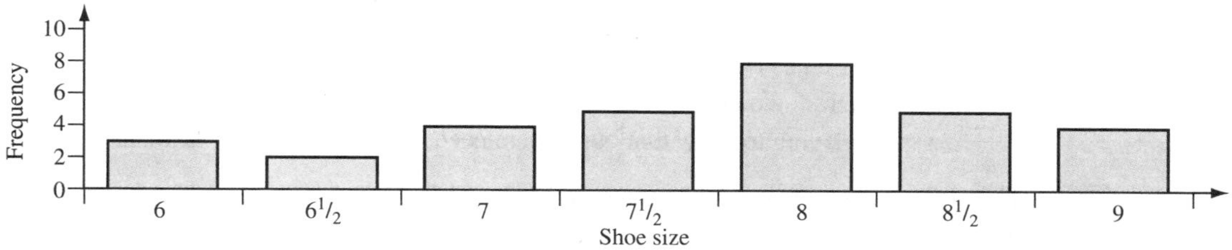

a How many students wear size $7\frac{1}{2}$ shoes?

b How many students were in the survey?

c What is the most common shoe size?

d Can you tell how many boys were in the survey? Explain your answer.

3 The table shows the lowest and highest marks six students got in a series of mental arithmetic tests.

	Rana	Ben	Chris	Dave	Emma	Ade
Lowest mark	7	11	10	10	15	9
Highest mark	11	12	12	13	16	14

Draw a dual bar chart to illustrate the data.

F

4 The following data shows the times, to the nearest minute, that patients had to wait before seeing a doctor.

5	12	14	24	32	7	12	35	23	27	13	6
28	4	20	13	40	5	2	11	16	31	10	26
25	30	29	9	12	27	13	20	24	11	14	38

a Draw a grouped frequency table to show the waiting times of the patients, using class intervals 1–10, 11–20 , 21–30, 31–40.

b Draw a bar chart to illustrate the data.

5 Richard did a survey to find out which brand of crisps his friends preferred. He drew this bar chart to illustrate his data.

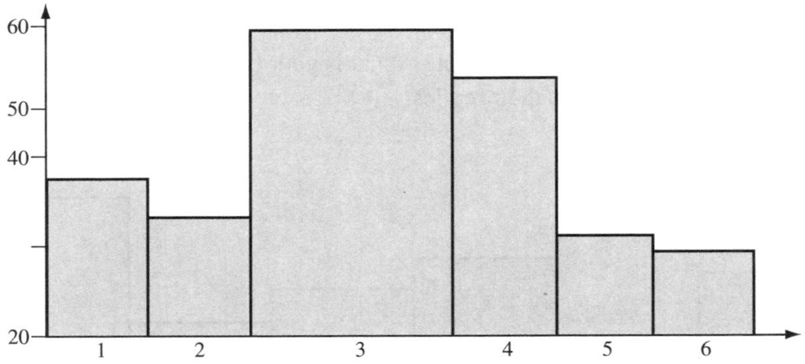

Richard's bar chart is very misleading. Explain how he could improve it and then redraw it, taking into account all your improvements.

FM 6 This table shows the number of accidents involving buses that have occurred in the town of Redlow over a six year period.

Year	2004	2005	2006	2007	2008	2009
No. of accidents	13	17	14	18	13	19

a Draw a pictogram from this data.

b Draw a bar chart from this data.

c Which diagram would you use if you were going to write an article for the local newspaper trying to show that bus drivers need to take more care? Explain your answer.

PS 7 The class was given a mental maths problem-solving test by Mr Ball. The bar chart shows the results.

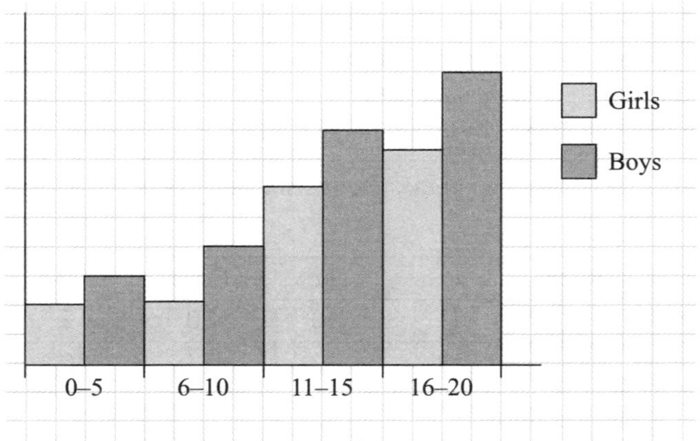

Mr Ball says, 'The boys seem to do better than the girls.' How much better are the boys than the girls?

AU **8** The bar chart shows the rainfall of two major cities in Wales and England over three years.

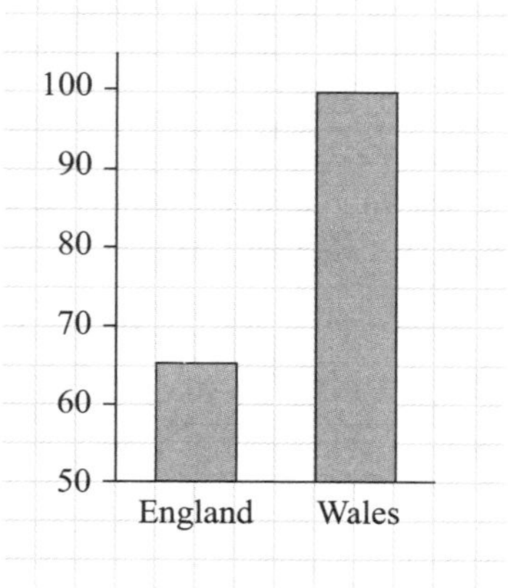

Elwyn says, 'There is more than three times as much rain in Wales than there is in England.'
Is Elwyn correct?
Explain your answer.

5.4 Line graphs

HOMEWORK 5D

1 The line graph shows the monthly average exchange rate of the Japanese Yen for £1 over a six month period.

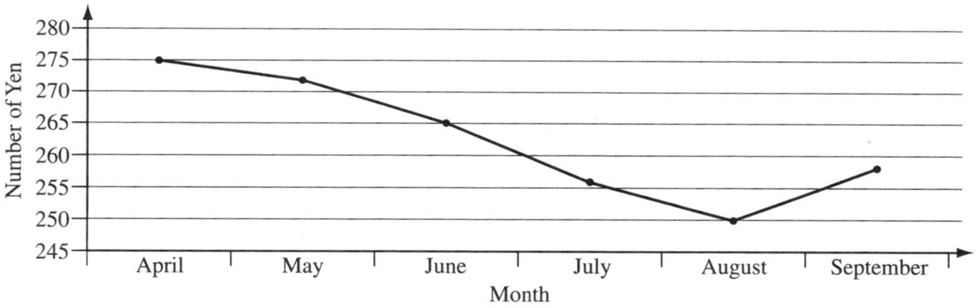

a In which month was the lowest exchange rate and what was that value?
b By how much did the exchange rate fall from April to August?
c Which month had the greatest fall in the exchange rate from the previous month?
d Mr Hargreaves changed £200 into Yen during July. How many Yen did he receive?

2 The table shows the temperature in Cuzco in Peru over a 24-hour period.

Time	0000	0400	0800	1200	1600	2000	2400
Temperature (°C)	1	–4	6	15	21	9	–1

a Draw a line graph for the data.
b From your graph estimate the temperature at 1800.

D

3 The table shows the value, to the nearest million pounds, of a country's imports and exports.

Year	2004	2005	2006	2007	2008	2009
Imports	22	35	48	51	62	55
Exports	35	41	56	53	63	58

a Draw line graphs on the same axes to show the imports and exports of the country.
b Find the smallest and greatest difference between the imports and exports.

FM 4 The table shows the estimated number of passengers travelling by train in a country.

Year	1970	1975	1980	1985	1990	1995	2000	2005
Train passengers (thousands)	210	310	450	570	590	650	690	770

a Draw a line graph showing this data.
b From your graph, estimate the number of passengers in 2010.
c Between which two consecutive years did the number of train passengers increase the most?
d Explain the trend in the numbers of train passengers. What reason can you suggest to explain this trend?

PS 5 The height of a baby giraffe is measured at the end of each week.

Week	1	2	3	4	5
Height (cm)	110	160	200	220	235

Estimate the height of the giraffe after 6 weeks.

AU 6 When plotting a graph to show the number of people attending cricket matches at Headingley, Kevin decided to start his graph at 18 000.
Explain why he might have done that.

5.5 Stem-and-leaf diagrams

HOMEWORK 5E

E

1 The following stem-and-leaf diagram shows the number of TVs a retailer sold daily over a three week period.

1	2 8 9
2	0 2 4 4 4 4 5 7 8 8 9
3	1 2 4 8

Key 1 | 2 represents 12 TVs

a What is the greatest number of TVs the retailer sold in one day?
b What is the most common number of TVs sold daily?
c What is the difference between the greatest number and the least number of TVs sold?

2 The following stem-and-leaf diagram shows the ages of a group of people waiting for a train at a station.

1	6 8 9
2	4 7 8 9
3	0 2 4 5 6
4	2 5 5 6 8
5	0 4 8

Key 1 | 6 represents an age of 16

a How many people were waiting for a train?
b What is the age of the youngest person?
c What is the difference in age between the youngest person and oldest person?

3 A survey is carried out to find the speed, in miles per hour, of 30 vehicles travelling on a motorway. The results are shown below.

62 45 70 58 68 70 75 80 72 65 40 55 65 72 38
70 75 68 50 48 65 60 68 72 70 45 68 69 68 60

a Show the data on an ordered stem-and-leaf diagram. (Remember to show a key.)
b What is the most common speed?
c What is the difference between the greatest speed and the lowest speed?

FM 4 A teacher has given her class a spelling test. She wants to compare the results of boys and girls. To do this she puts the results in a stem-and-leaf table.

Boys		Girls
5 3 1 2	1	4 6 8
8 8 5 1	2	1 1 2 7 7 7
6 5 5 5	3	0 0 4

Key: Boys 2 | 1 means 12 correct
Girls 1 | 4 means 14 correct

a What was the highest number correct for the boys?
b What was the lowest number correct for the girls?
c What was the most common correct number correct for:
i Boys **ii** Girls?
d Overall, who did better in the tests – boys or girls?
Give a reason for your answer.

PS 5 The following data is gathered about the girls' and boys' IQ test scores in a form.
Boys: 117 105 128 132 110 108 123 114 128 110
Girls: 122 137 113 118 131 129 104 120 117 134
Present these scores in an appropriate way for them to be compared.

AU 6 Godwin was asked to create a stem-and-leaf diagram from some numerical data, but he said, 'It is impossible to do this sensibly!'
Give an example of 10 items of numerical data that could not sensibly be put into a stem-and-leaf diagram.

Functional Maths Activity

Wine buying in the UK

This table shows the number of cases of different types of wine bought in the UK over the last few years.

	Number of cases (millions)				
Wines	**2005**	**2006**	**2007**	**2008**	**2009**
Chardonnay	6	8	8	8	8
Pinot Grigio	2	3	4	5	5
Sauvignon Blanc	3	4	5	5	6
Merlot	4	4	5	4	5
Shiraz	3	3	4	5	5
Cabernet Sauvignon	4	5	4	5	5
Rioja	2	2	2	2	2

Use appropriate statistical diagrams and measures to summarise the data given in the table. Then write a report about the sales of wines in the UK over these five years.

6 Geometry and measures: Scale and drawing

6.1 Reading scales

HOMEWORK 6A

1 Read the values from the following scales. Remember to state the units.

a

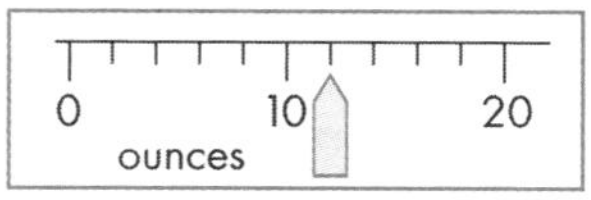

b

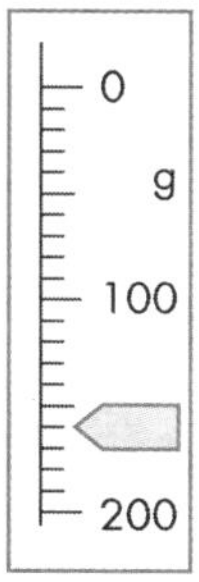

c

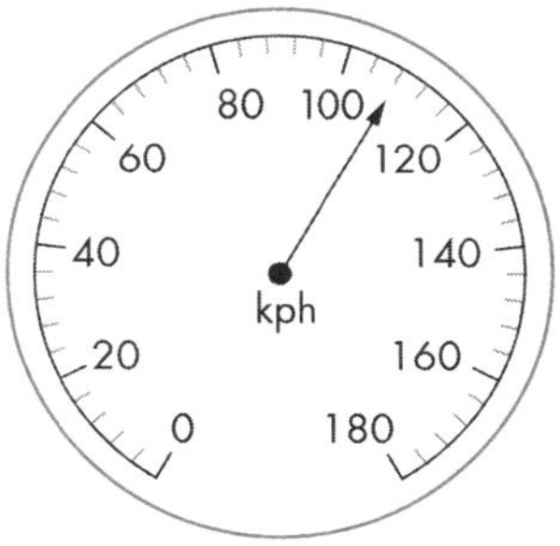

d

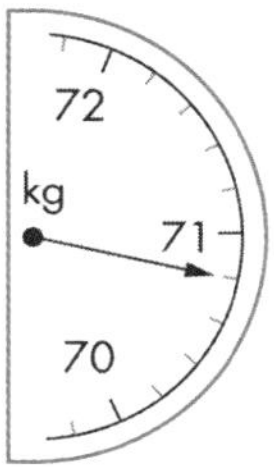

2 Read the temperatures shown on each of these thermometers.

a

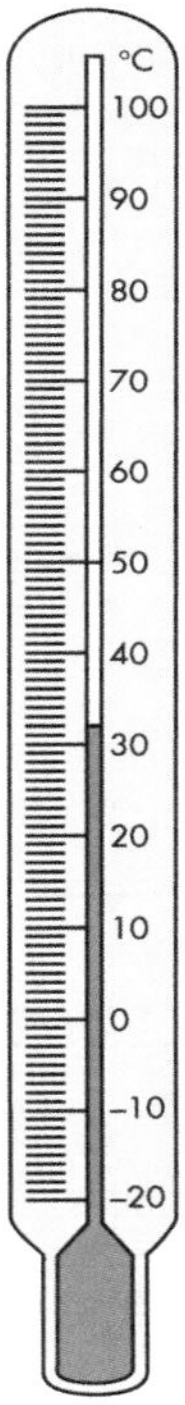

b

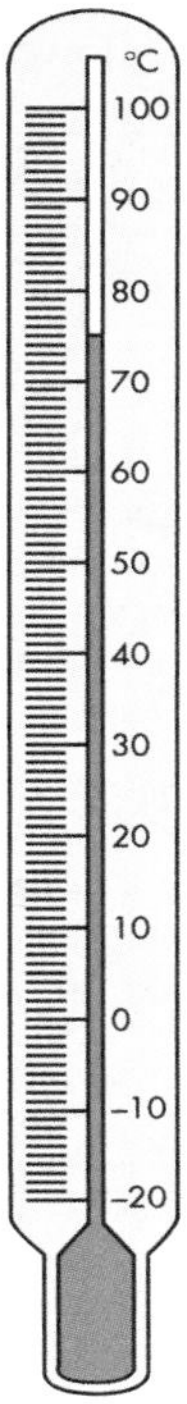

c

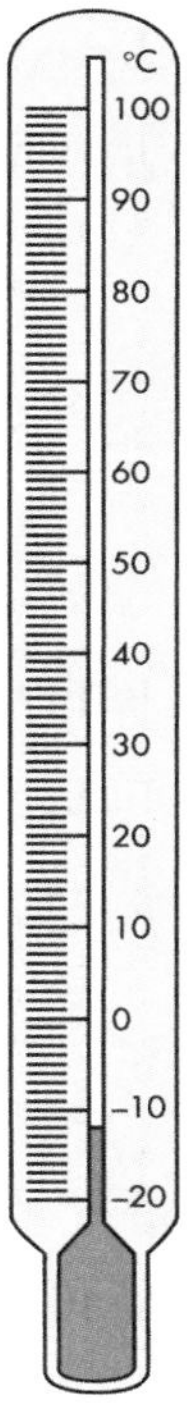

3 Read the values shown on these scales.

a

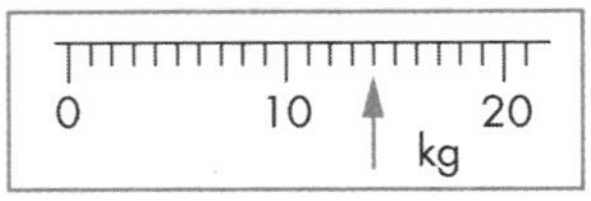

b

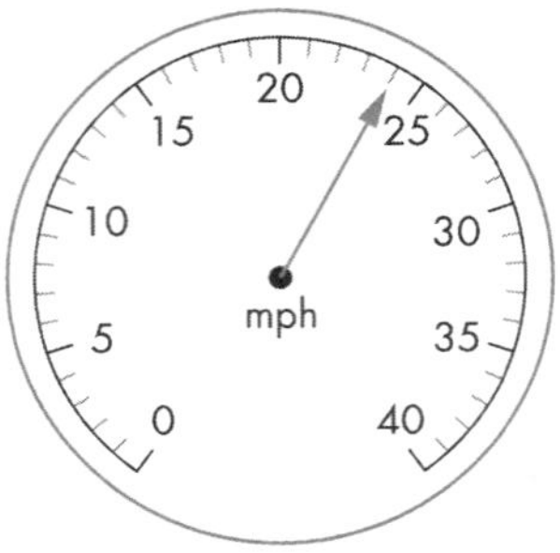

c

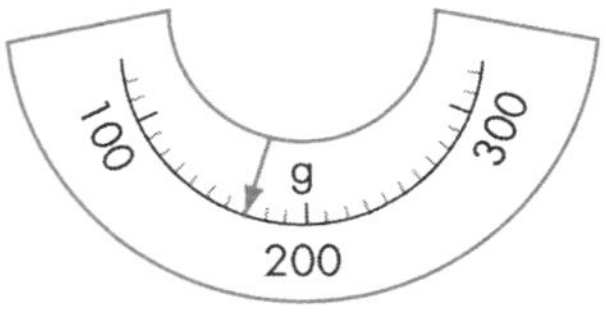

d

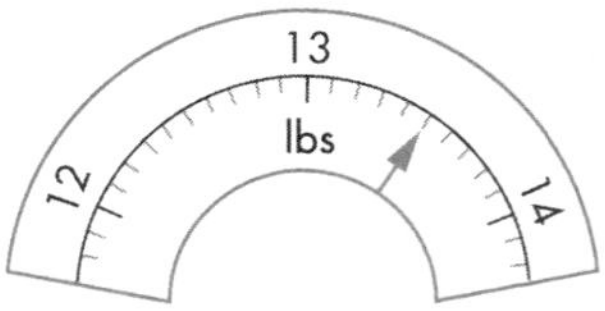

4 The speedometer below shows speeds in mph and km/h.

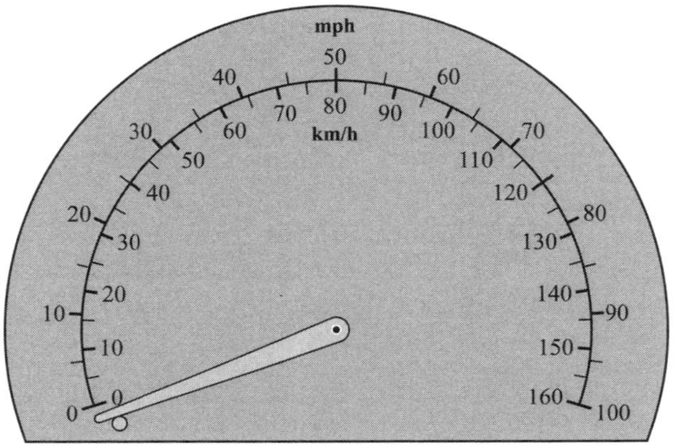

a Use the scale on the speedometer to change 50mph into km/h.

b Use the scale on the speedometer to change 120km/h into mph.

FM 5 Joe is going on holiday. He is allowed to take a suitcase weighing 15 kg.

Joe stands on the bathroom scales first on his own and then holding his suitcase.

Is his suitcase too heavy?

PS 6 Each of these three lines is 10 cm long.

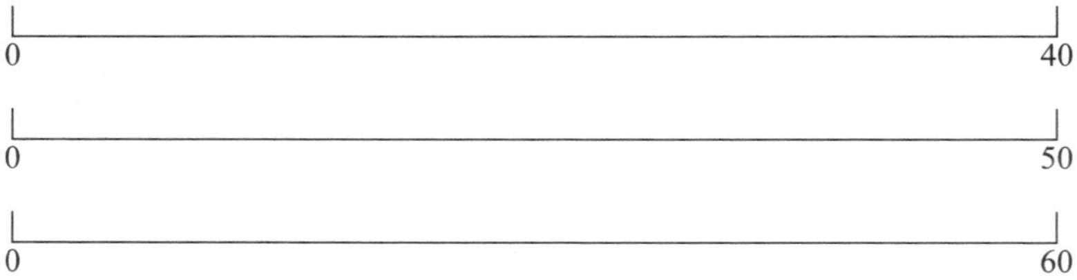

Copy the lines and mark each one with an arrow pointing to a value of 30.

AU 7 The diagram shows part of a scale.

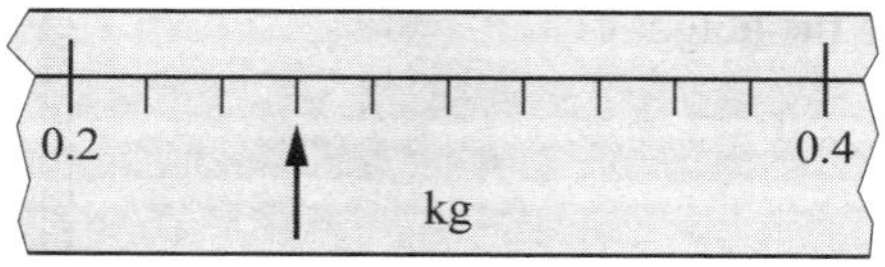

Lisa says that the arrow is pointing to 0.23 kg.
Explain why she is wrong.

6.2 Sensible estimates

HOMEWORK 6B

1 The picture shows a teacher standing by a whiteboard in a classroom.

a Estimate the height of the door.
b Estimate the length of the classroom.
c Estimate the length and width of the whiteboard.

AU 2 Estimate the height of the giraffe.

3

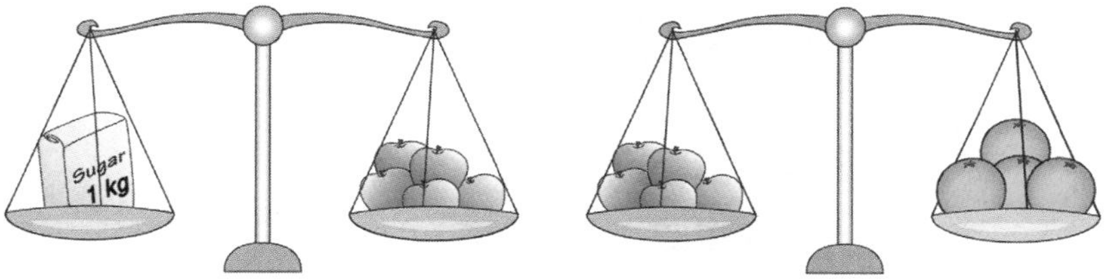

a Estimate the weight of one apple.
b Estimate the weight of one orange.

F

PS 4 The height of The London Eye is 135 m.
Use this information to estimate the height of:

a The Eiffel Tower
b Sears Tower
c Warszawa Radio Mast.

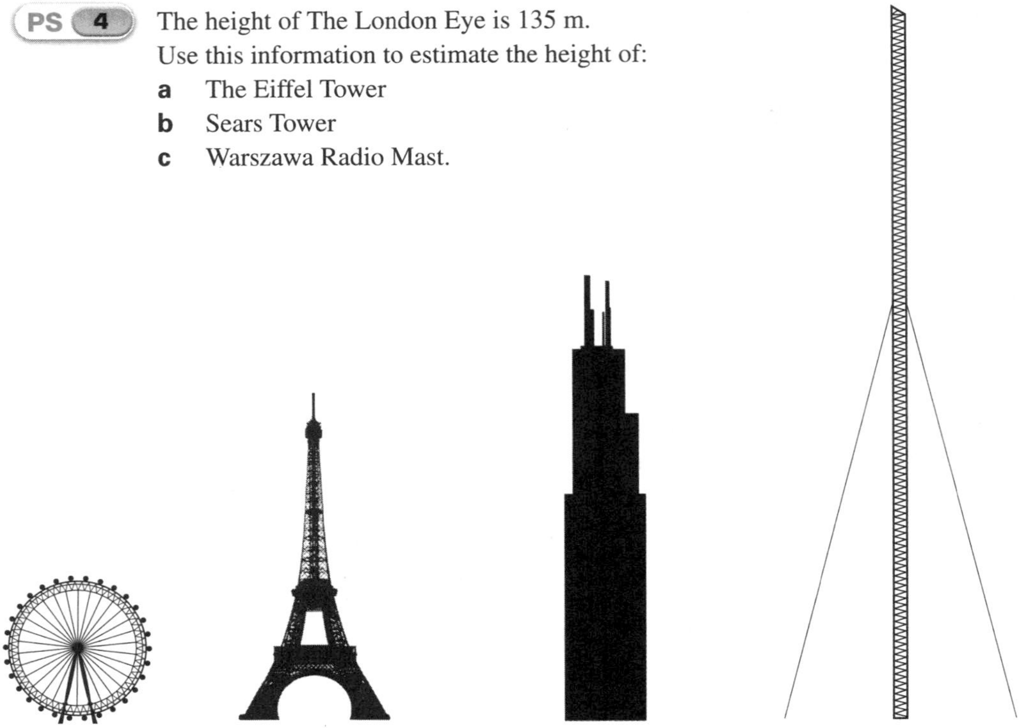

London Eye | Eiffel Tower | Sears Tower | Warszawa Radio Mast

FM 5 A builder wants to estimate the height of a lighthouse.

Use the picture to estimate the height.

6.3 Scale drawings

HOMEWORK 6C

1 The grid below shows the floor plan of a kitchen. The scale is 1 cm to 30 cm.

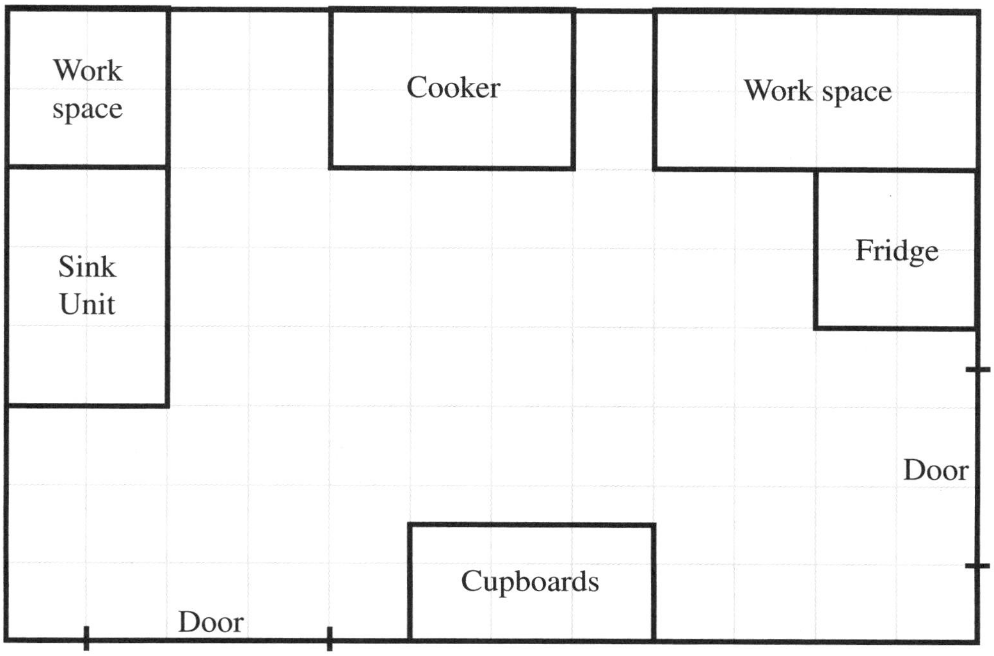

a State the actual dimensions of:
- **i** the sink unit
- **ii** the cooker
- **iii** the fridge
- **iv** the cupboards.

b Calculate the actual total area of the work space.

2 Below is a sketch of a ladder leaning against a wall.

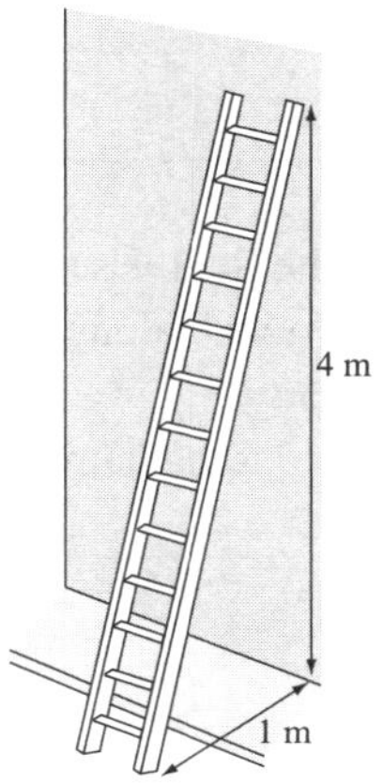

The bottom of the ladder is 1 m away from the wall and it reaches 4 m up the wall.

a Make a scale drawing to show the position of the ladder. Use a scale of 4 cm to 1 m.

b Use your scale drawing to work out the actual length of the ladder.

F

3 The map below is drawn to a scale of 1 cm to 2 km.

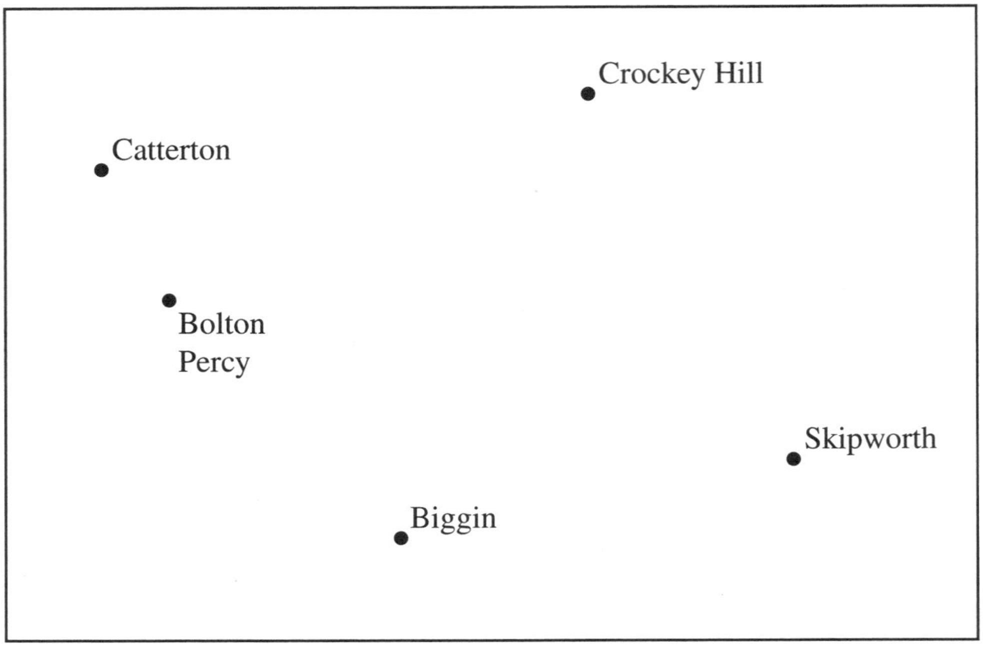

Find the distances between:

a Biggin and Skipworth

b Bolton Percy and Crockey Hill

c Skipworth and Catterton

d Crockey Hill and Biggin

e Catterton and Bolton Percy.

FM 4 A farmer draws a sketch for one of his fields. This is his diagram.

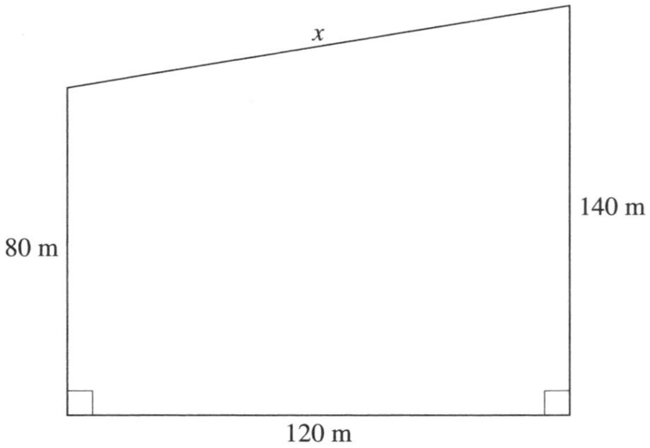

a Make a scale drawing of the field. Use the scale 1 cm represents 20 m.

b The farmer wants to build a wall along the side marked x on the diagram. Each metre length of wall uses 60 bricks.
Use your diagram to work out the number of bricks the farmer will need.

5 The map below shows the position of four fells in the Lake District. The map is drawn to a scale of 1 : 150 000.

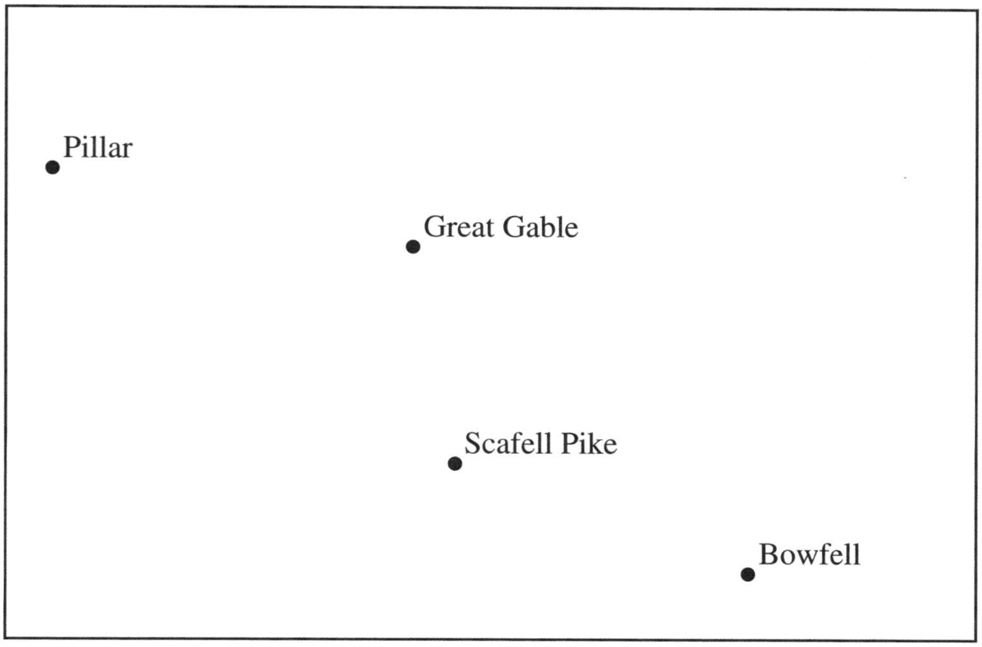

State the following distances to the nearest kilometre:

a Scafell Pike to Great Gable
b Scafell Pike to Pillar
c Great Gable to Pillar
d Pillar to Bowfell
e Bowfell to Great Gable

6 Here is a scale drawing of a ferry crossing a river from port A to port B. The width of the river is 400 m.

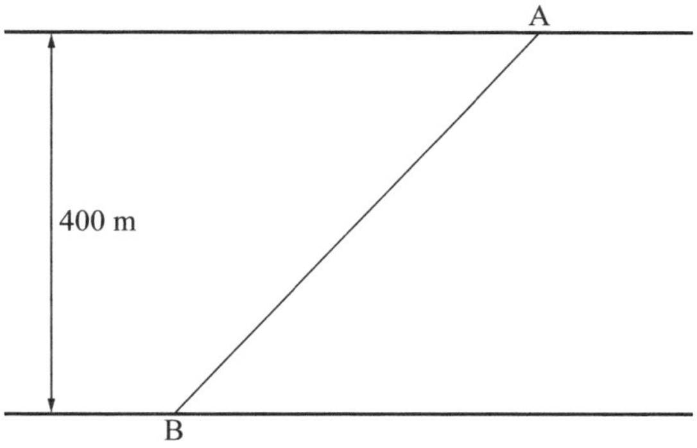

a Which of the following is the correct scale for the drawing?
i 1 : 1000 **ii** 1 : 10 000 **iii** 1 : 40 000 **iv** 1 : 100 000

b What is the actual distance from port A to port B?

6.4 Nets

HOMEWORK 6D

F

1 Four nets are shown below. Copy the nets that would make a cube.

a

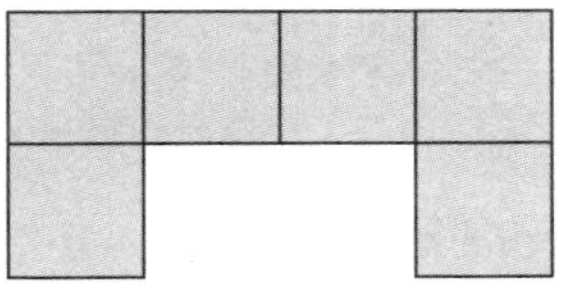

b

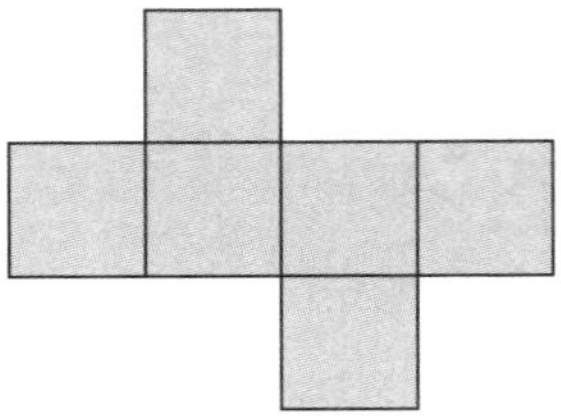

c

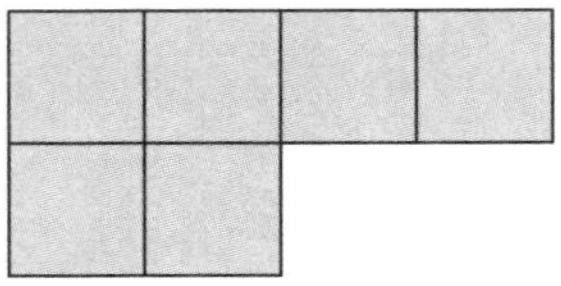

d

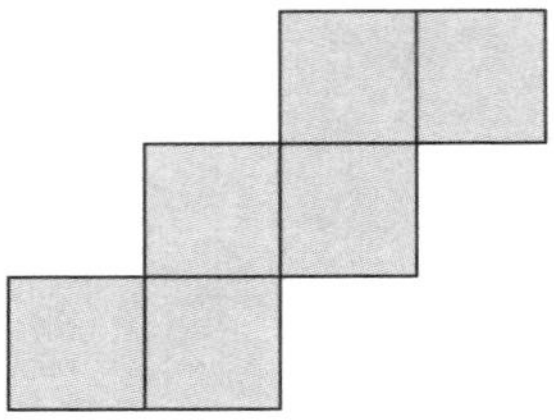

2 Draw, on squared paper, an accurate net for each of these cuboids.

a

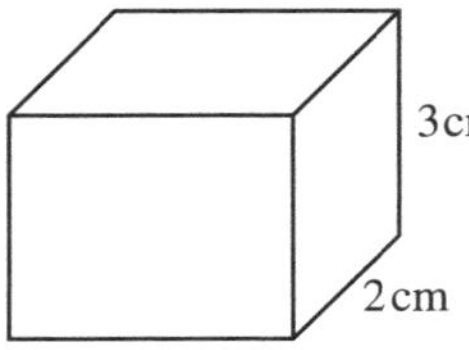

b

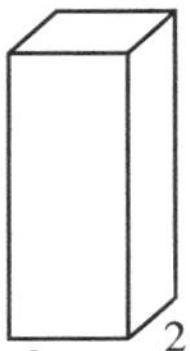

E

3 Draw, on squared paper, an accurate net for this triangular prism.

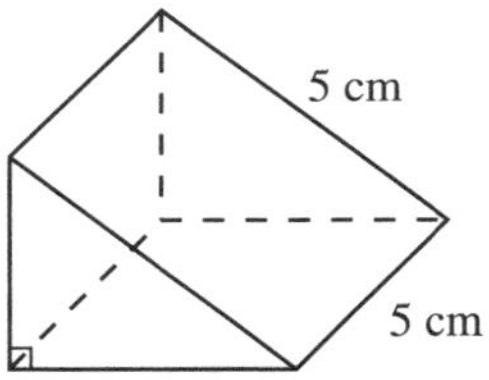

4 The diagram shows a sketch of a square-based pyramid.

a Write down how many of each of the following the pyramid has:

i vertices

ii edges

iii faces.

b Draw a sketch for the net of the pyramid.

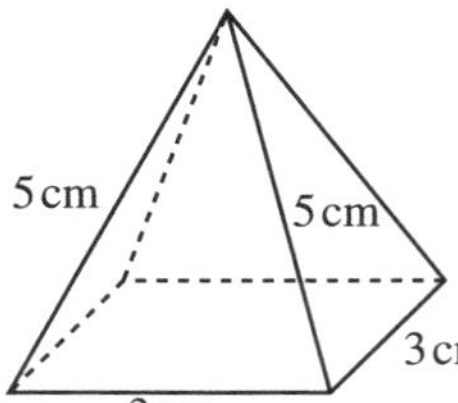

E

FM 5 Paul is making this dice out of card.

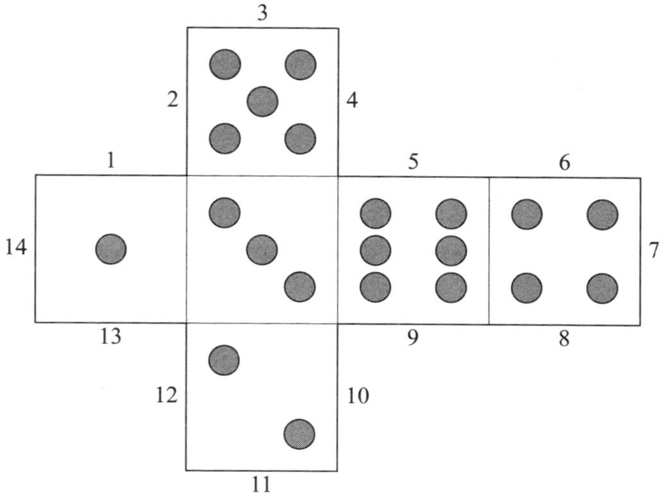

Before he cuts it out, he needs to know which edges join together so that he can put on tabs. For example, edge 1 joins with edge 2.
List the other pairs of edges that join together.

PS 6 This is a diagram of a regular tetrahedron.

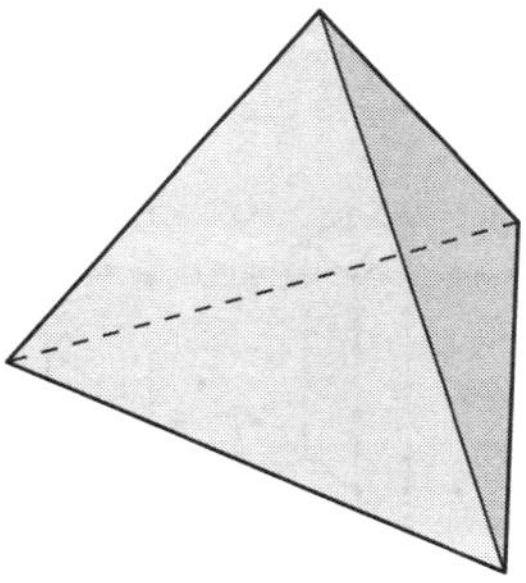

It is made up of four identical equilateral triangles.
A tetrahedron has two nets. Can you draw them both?

AU 7 Zoë has five shapes:

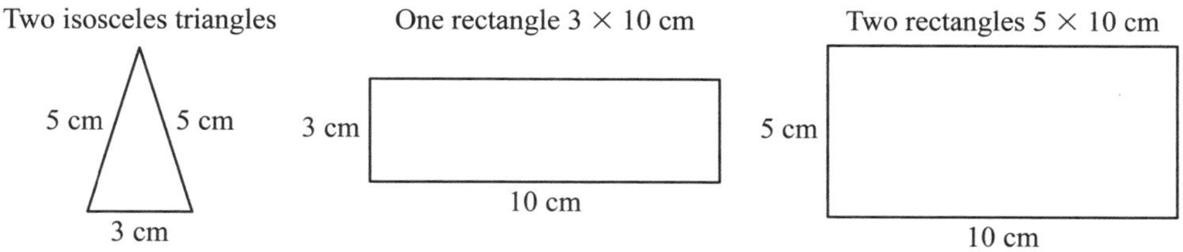

Draw a sketch to show how she can put the five shapes together to make a net of a triangular prism.

6.5 Using an isometric grid

HOMEWORK 6E

1 Draw accurately each of these cuboids on an isometric grid.

a

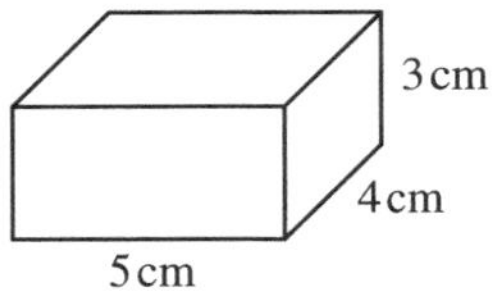

b

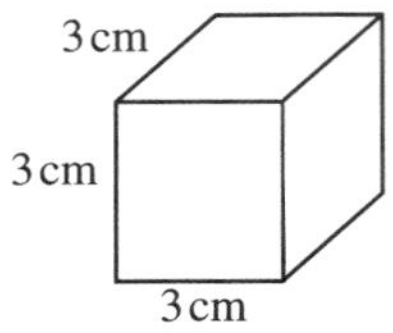

2 Draw accurately each of these 3D shapes on an isometric grid.

a

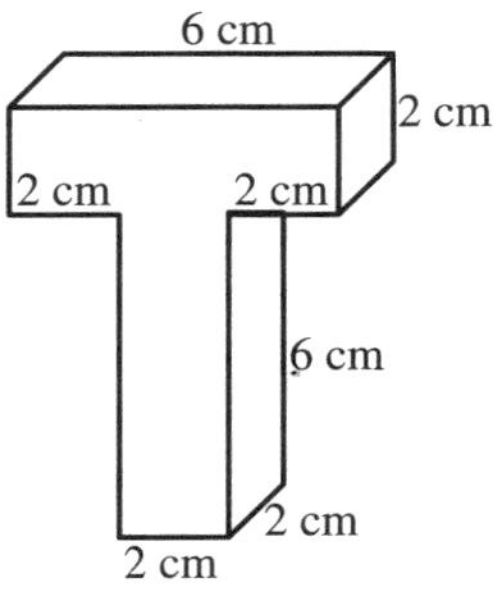

b

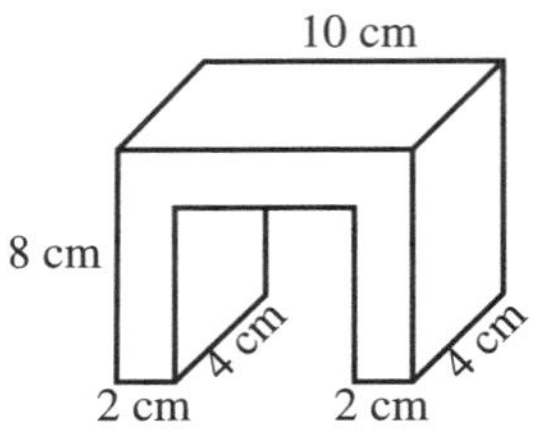

3 For each of the following 3D shapes, draw on squared paper:

i the plan **ii** the front elevation **iii** the side elevation.

a

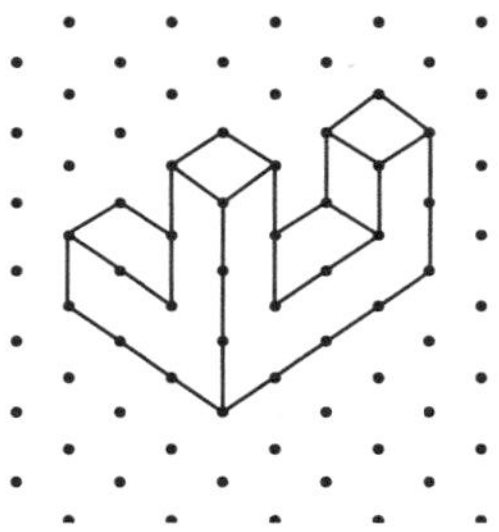

b

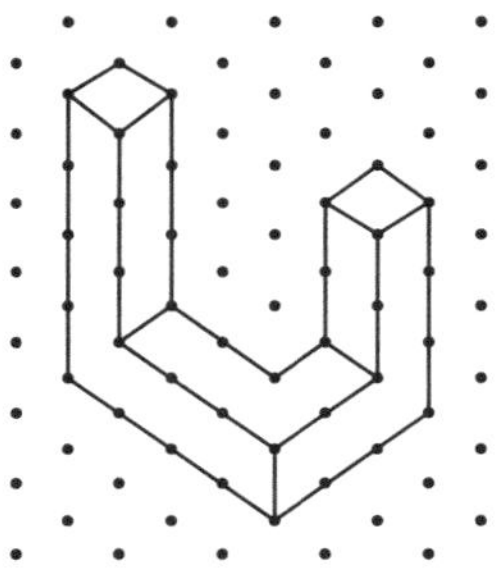

PS 4 Here are three views of a 3D shape.

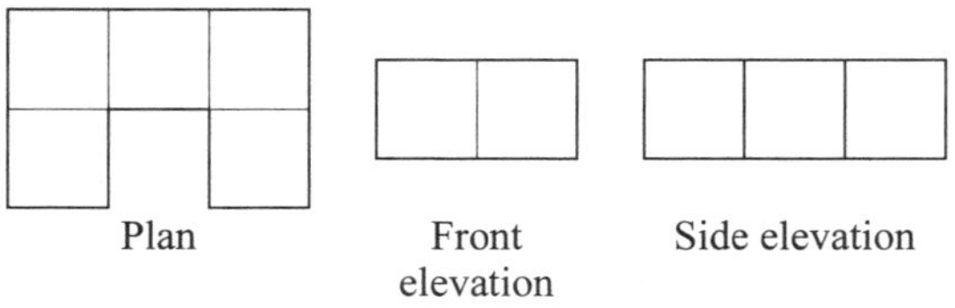

Draw the 3D shape on an isometric grid.

AU 5 This solid shape is made from cubes.

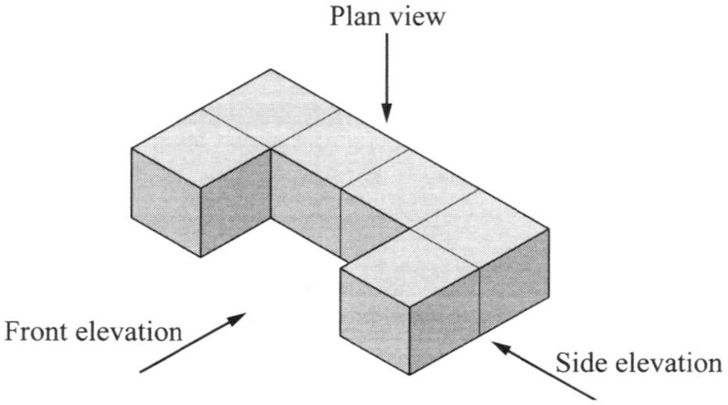

Here are some diagrams of the shape.

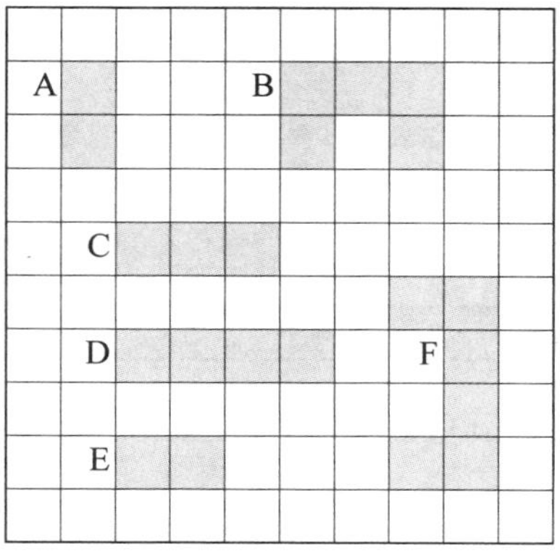

a Which is the plan view?

b Which is the front elevation?

c Which is the side elevation?

Functional Maths Activity

Logo design

A firm called Trader Limited wants to design a logo for their company. An artist designs the following logo, which is drawn on isometric paper.

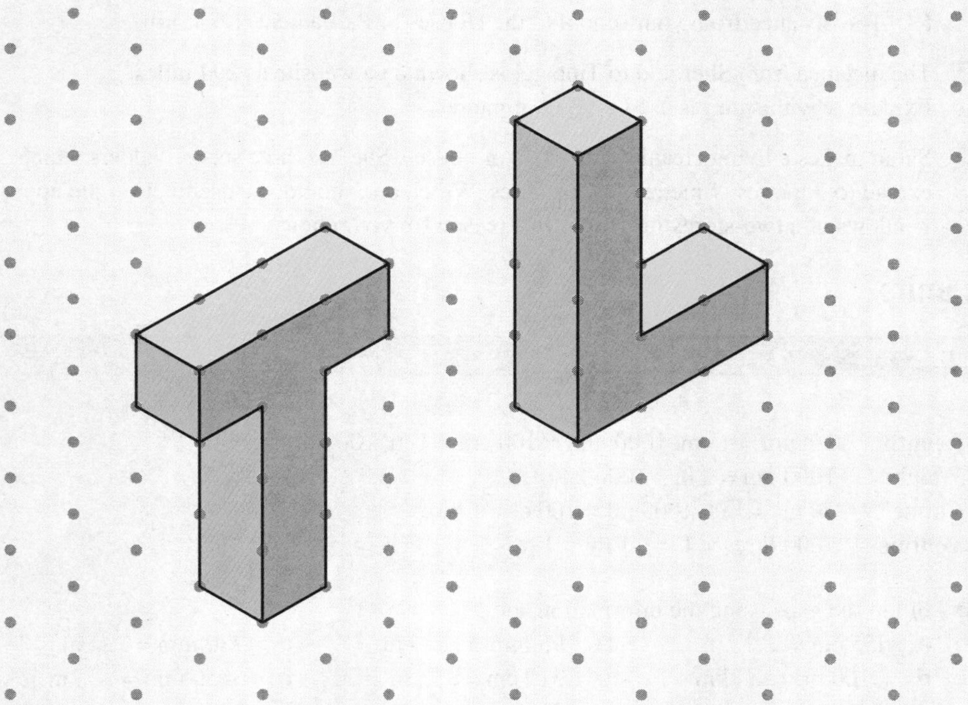

On isometric paper, design a logo for a company called 'Fisher Home Incorporated'.

7 Measures: Units

7.1 Systems of measurement

HOMEWORK 7A

G

1 Decide which metric unit you would most likely use to measure each of the following amounts.

a The height of your best friend.
b The distance from school to your home.
c The thickness of a CD.
d The weight of your maths teacher.
e The amount of water in a lake.
f The weight of a slice of bread.
g The length of a double-decker bus.
h The weight of a kitten.

F

2 Estimate the approximate metric length, weight or capacity of each of the following.

a This book (both length and weight).
b The length of the road you live on. (You do not need to walk along it all.)
c The capacity of a bottle of wine (metric measure).
d A door (length, width and weight).
e The diameter of a £1 coin, and its weight.
f The distance from your school to the Houses of Parliament (London).

AU 3 The distance from Sheffield to Tintagel is shown on a website as 294 miles. Explain why this unit is used instead of metres.

FM 4 Sarah makes a living cleaning windows of houses. She has three sets of ladders which extend to 2 metres, 4 metres and 6 metres. Which one should she use to clean the upper windows of a two-storey house? Give a reason for your choice.

7.2 Metric units

HOMEWORK 7B

Length	10 mm = 1 cm, 1000 mm = 100 cm = 1 m, 1000 m = 1 km
Weight	1000 gm = 1 kg , 1000 kg = 1 t
Capacity	10 ml = 1 cl, 1000 ml = 100 cl = 1 litre
Volume	1000 litres = 1 m^3, 1 ml = 1 cl^3

F

1 Fill in the gaps using the information above.

a 155 cm = ... m
b 95 mm = ... cm
c 780 mm = ... m
d 3100 m = ... km
e 310 cm = ... m
f 3050 mm = ... m
g 156 mm = ... cm
h 2180 m = ... km
i 1070 mm = ... m
j 1324 cm = ... m
k 175 m = ... km
l 83 mm = ... m
m 620 mm = ... cm
n 2130 cm = ... m
o 5120 m = ... km
p 8150 g = ... kg
q 2300 kg = ... t
r 32 ml = ... cl
s 1360 ml = ... l
t 580 cl = ... l
u 950 kg = ... t

2 Fill in the gaps using the information at the start of Homework 7B.

a	120 g = ... kg	**b**	150 ml = ... l	**c**	350 cl = ... l
d	540 ml = ... cl	**e**	2060 kg = ... t	**f**	7500 ml = ... l
g	3800 g = ... kg	**h**	605 cl = ... l	**i**	15 ml = ... l
j	6300 l = ... m^3	**k**	45 ml = ... cm^3	**l**	2350 l = ... m^3
m	720 l = ... m^3	**n**	8.2 m = ... cm	**o**	71 km = ... m
p	8.6 m = ... mm	**q**	15.6 cm = ... mm	**r**	0.83 m = ... cm
s	5.15 km = ... m	**t**	1.85 cm = ... mm	**u**	2.75 m = ... cm

FM 3 Alesha wants to put up six shelves, each 65 cm long. She finds that she can buy planks of the correct width in three different lengths: 1200 mm, 1800 mm and 2400 mm. What should she buy to have the least amount of waste wood?

PS 4 Find how many square centimetres there are in a square kilometre.

AU 5 Could you pour all the water from a full 2 litre bottle into a container whose volume you know to be 101 cm^3?
Explain how you know.

7.3 Imperial units

HOMEWORK 7C

Length	12 inches = 1 foot, 3 feet = 1 yard, 1760 yards = 1 mile
Weight	16 ounces = 1 pound, 14 pounds = 1 stone, 2240 pounds = 1 ton
Capacity	8 pints = 1 gallon

1 Fill in the gaps using the information above.

a	5 feet = ... inches	**b**	5 yards = ... feet
c	3 miles = ... yards	**d**	6 pounds = ... ounces
e	5 stones = ... pounds	**f**	2 tons = ... pounds
g	4 gallons = ... pints	**h**	7 feet = ... inches
i	2 yards = ... inches	**j**	11 yards = ... feet
k	5 pounds = ... ounces	**l**	39 feet = ... yards
m	2 stones = ... ounces	**n**	4400 yards = ... miles
o	12 gallons = ... pints	**p**	2 miles = ... feet
q	84 inches = ... feet	**r**	48 ounces = ... pounds
s	21 feet = ... yards	**t**	22 400 pounds = ... tons
u	2 miles = ... inches	**v**	256 ounces = ... pounds
w	80 pints = ... gallons	**x**	280 pounds = ... stones
y	31 680 feet = ... miles	**z**	2 tons = ... ounces

PS 2 Find how many square feet are in a square mile.

FM 3 Running tracks in the UK and the USA used to be 400 yards long. How many times would you need to run around the track in a six-mile race?

AU 4 1 pound is approximately 450 grams.
Explain how you know that 1 tonne is lighter than 1 ton.

F E E D

7.4 Conversion factors

HOMEWORK 7D

Length	Weight	Capacity
1 metre ≈ 39 inches	2.2 pounds ≈ 1 kilogram	1 litre ≈ 1.75 pints
1 foot ≈ 30 centimetres		1 gallon ≈ 4.5 litres
1 foot ≈ 12 inches		
5 miles ≈ 8 kilometres		

F

1 Change each of these weights in kilograms to pounds.
a 6 **b** 8 **c** 15 **d** 32 **e** 45

2 Change each of these weights in pounds to kilograms. (Give each answer to 1 decimal place.)
a 10 **b** 18 **c** 25 **d** 40 **e** 56

3 Change each of these capacities in litres to pints.
a 2 **b** 8 **c** 25 **d** 60 **e** 75

4 Change each of these capacities in pints to litres. (Give each answer to the nearest litre.)
a 7 **b** 20 **c** 35 **d** 42 **e** 100

5 Change each of these distances in miles to kilometres.
a 20 **b** 30 **c** 50 **d** 65 **e** 120

6 Change each of these distances in kilometres to miles.
a 16 **b** 24 **c** 40 **d** 72 **e** 300

7 Change each of these capacities in gallons to litres.
a 5 **b** 12 **c** 27 **d** 50 **e** 72

8 Change each of these capacities in litres to gallons.
a 18 **b** 45 **c** 72 **d** 270 **e** 900

9 Change each of these distances in metres to inches.
a 2 **b** 5 **c** 8 **d** 10 **e** 12

10 Change each of these distances in feet to centimetres.
a 3 **b** 5 **c** 7 **d** 10 **e** 30

11 Change each of these distances in inches to metres. (Give your answer to 1 decimal place.)
a 48 **b** 52 **c** 60 **d** 75 **e** 100

E

FM **12** While on holiday in Iceland, I saw a road sign that said 'Blue Lagoon 26 km'.
I was in a coach travelling on a road with a speed limit of 40 km/h.
a Approximately how many miles was I from the Blue Lagoon?
b What was the speed limit in miles per hour?
c If the coach travelled at this top speed, how long would it take us to get to the Blue Lagoon? Give your answer in minutes.

C

FM PS **13** While cycling up the Alps, Tom had a 60 km stretch to cycle in one day. He knew that he could only average 11.5 mph on these hills in the Alps.
How long would he expect this stretch to take him with no stops?

AU **14** How many cubic inches are in a five gallon drum?

Functional Maths Activity

Olde English Units

Most units of measurement were originally based on parts of the body.
In the old days in Britain, there were some very strange units used.

a These units were used in the old days to measure cloth:

Cloth measures	
in	$2\frac{1}{4}$ inches = 1 nail
nl	4 nails = 1 quarter
qr	4 quarters = 1 yard (yd)
Fl. e	3 quarters = 1 Flemish ell
Eng. e	5 quarters = 1 English ell
Fr. e	6 quarters = 1 French ell
Sc. e	37 in = 1 Scotch ell

Work out the lengths of the following in centimetres.
Give your answers to the nearest centimetre.

i A Flemish Ell
ii An English Ell
iii A French Ell
iv A Scotch ell

b The following units were used in the old days to measure heaped goods.

Heaped measures for lime, coals, fish, potatoes, fruit, etc.	
gall	2 gallons = 1 peck
pks	4 pecks = 1 bushel
bush	3 bushel = 1 sack
sks	12 sacks = 1 Chaldron (chal.)

c These units were used in the old days to measure Yarn

Yarn Measures	
Cotton Yarn	Lint Yarn
54 inches = 1 thread	90 inches = 1 thread
80 threads = 1 skein or rap	120 threads = 1 cut
7 skeins = 1 hank	2 cuts = 1 heer
18 hanks = 1 spindle	6 heers = 1 hasp
	4 hasps = 1 spindle

How much longer, in metres, is a lint spindle than a cotton spindle?

8 Geometry: Symmetry

8.1 Lines of symmetry

HOMEWORK 8A

1 Copy these shapes and draw on the lines of symmetry for each one. If it will help you, use tracing paper or a mirror to check your answers.

a  **b**  **c** 

d 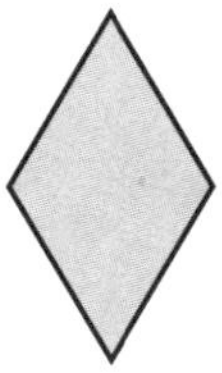 **e** 

2 Copy this regular hexagon and draw in all the lines of symmetry.

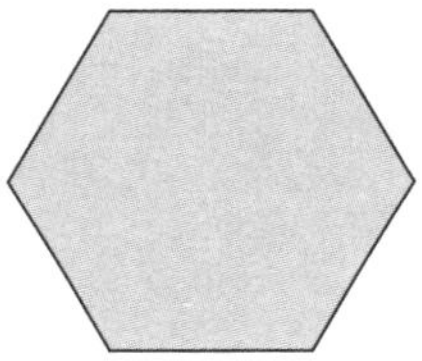

3 Copy these flow chart symbols and draw in all the lines of symmetry for each one.

a  **b** 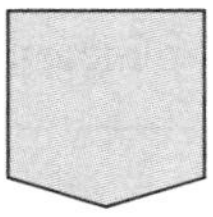 **c** 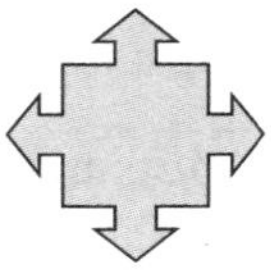

d 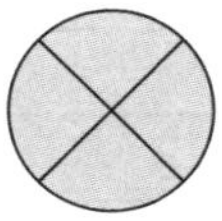 **e** 

4 Write down the number of lines of symmetry for each of these flags.

a  **b**  **c** 

5 How many lines of symmetry does each of these letters have?

a A **b** E **c** H **d** T **e** Y

AU 6 Draw three copies of the diagram on the right.

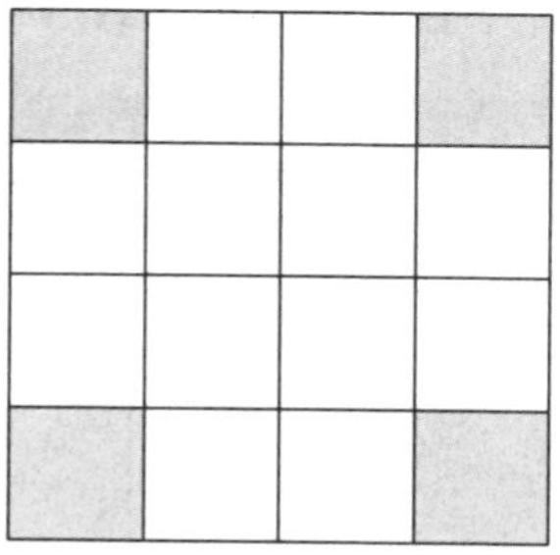

- **a** Shade in two more squares so that the diagram has no lines of symmetry.
- **b** Shade in two more squares so that the diagram has exactly one line of symmetry.
- **c** Shade in two more squares so that the diagram has exactly two lines of symmetry.

7 How many shapes can you find in this garden that have lines of symmetry?

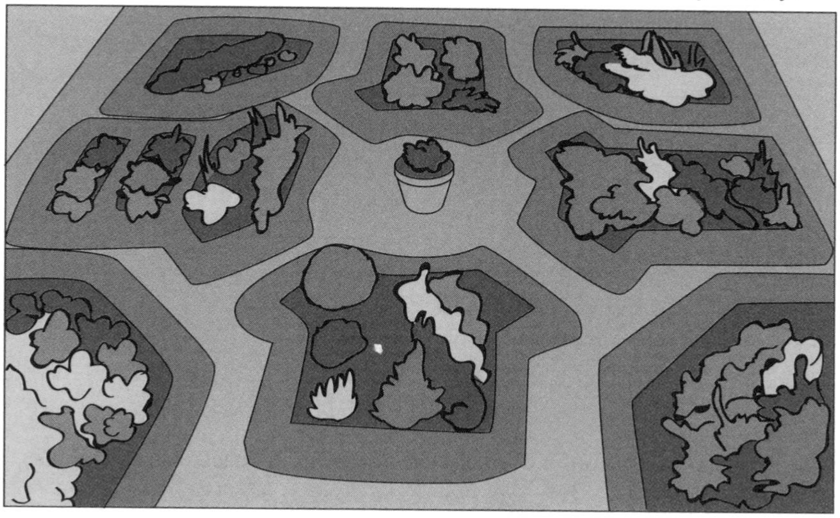

Draw each one and put on the lines of symmetry.

PS 8 Here is a grid and two rectangles.

- **a** On a copy of the grid, place the two rectangles so that the grid has one line of symmetry.
- **b** On another copy of the grid, place the two rectangles so that the grid has two lines of symmetry.

AU 9 Which shape is the odd one out?
Give a reason for your answer.

a

b

c

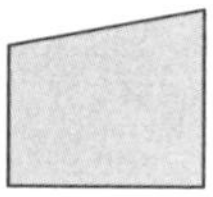

d

8.2 Rotational symmetry

HOMEWORK 8B

1 Copy these shapes and write below each one the order of rotational symmetry. If it will help you, use tracing paper.

a 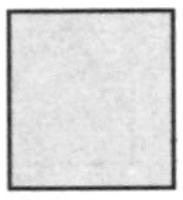
b 
c 
d 
e 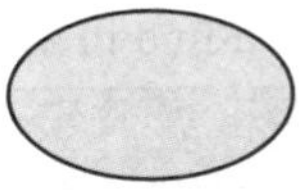

2 Write down the order of rotational symmetry for each of these shapes.

a 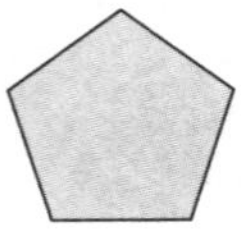
b 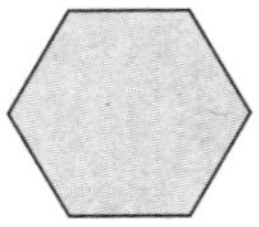
c 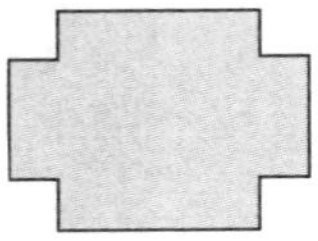
d 
e 

3 Write down the order of rotational symmetry for each of the symbols.

a 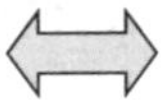
b 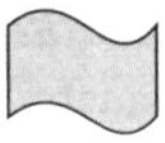
c 
d 
e 

4 The capital letter A fits exactly onto itself only once. So, its order of rotational symmetry is 1. This means that it has no rotational symmetry. Copy these capital letters and write the order of rotational symmetry below each one.

a E **b** H **c** I **d** L **e** N

f Q **g** S **h** Z

AU 5 Draw two copies of the diagram on the right.

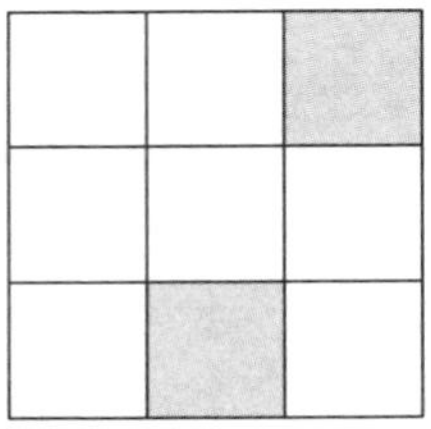

a Shade in two more squares so that the diagram has rotational symmetry of order 2 and no lines of symmetry.

b Shade in two more squares so that the diagram has rotational symmetry of order 1 and exactly 1 line of symmetry.

FM 6 These patterns are taken from old Turkish coins.
What is the order of rotational symmetry for each one?

a 
b 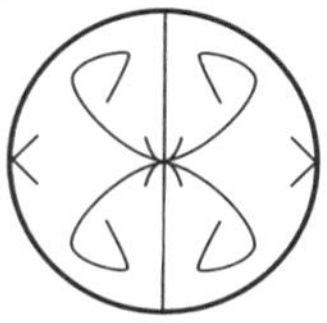
c 
d 

PS 7 On a copy of this shape, shade in four more squares so that the shape has rotational symmetry of order 2.

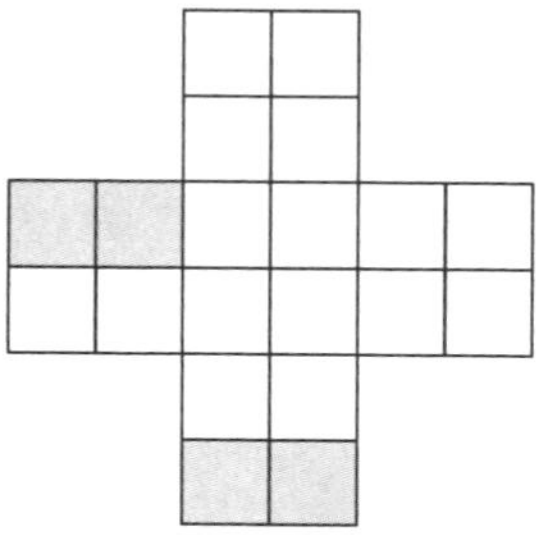

AU 8 Lizzie is drawing shapes that have rotational symmetry of order 3.
Here are some of her examples.

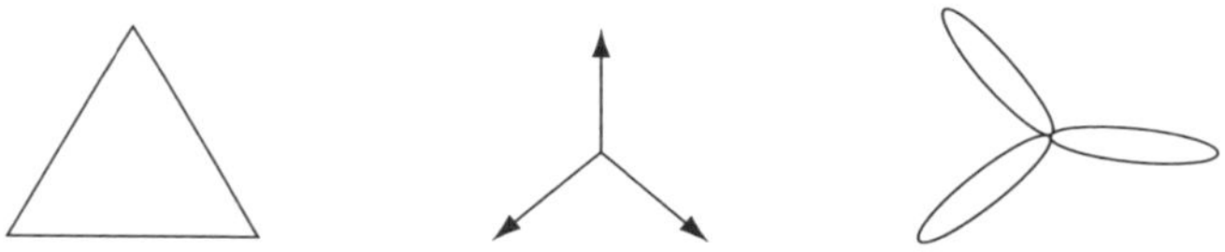

She says that all shapes that have rotational symmetry of order 3 must have three lines of symmetry.
Draw an example to show that she is wrong.

Functional Maths Activity

Symmetry in everyday life

What mathematical questions on symmetry could be asked about this picture?

9.1 Conversion graphs

HOMEWORK 9A

F

FM 1 A hire firm hired out large scanners. They used the following graph to approximate what the charges would be.

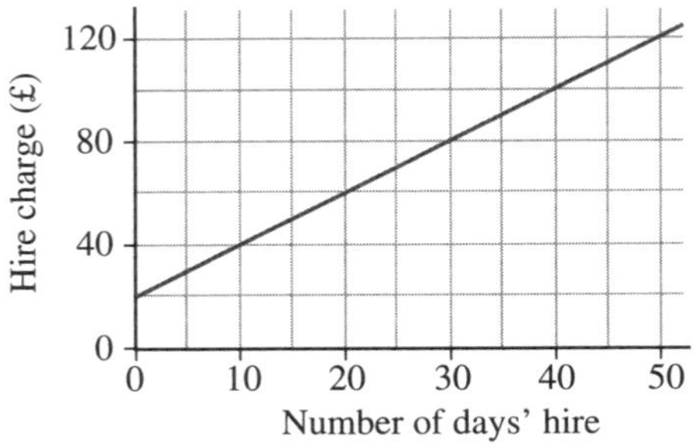

a Use the graph to find the approximate charge for hiring a scanner for:
i 20 days **ii** 30 days **iii** 50 days.

b Use the graph to find out how many days' hire you would get for a cost of:
i £120 **ii** £100 **iii** £70.

c Explain how you could use the graph to work out the cost for each day of hire.

FM 2 A conference centre used the following chart for the approximate cost of a conference based on the number of people attending it.

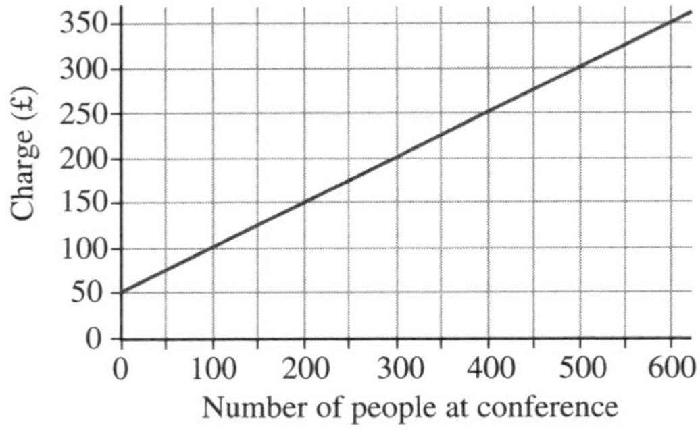

a Use the graph to find the approximate charge for:
i 500 people **ii** 300 people **iii** 250 people.

b Use the graph to estimate how many people can attend a conference at the centre for a cost of:
i £250 **ii** £150 **iii** £125.

c Explain how you could use the graph to work out the cost for each person.

FM **3** Jayne lost her fuel bill, but while talking to her friends, she found out that:

Kris who had used 750 units was charged £69
Nic who had used 250 units was charged £33
Shami who had used 500 units was charged £51.

a Plot the given information and draw a straight-line graph. Use a scale from 0 to 800 on the horizontal units axis, and from £0 to £70 on the vertical cost axis.

b Use your graph to find what Jayne will be charged for 420 units.

AU **4** This conversion graph shows the relationship between millilitres and American 'cups', which is a measure used in cooking.

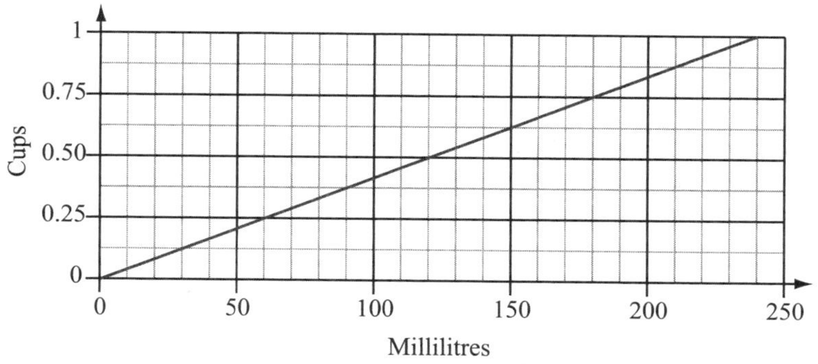

This conversion graph shows the relationship between millilitres and British fluid ounces.

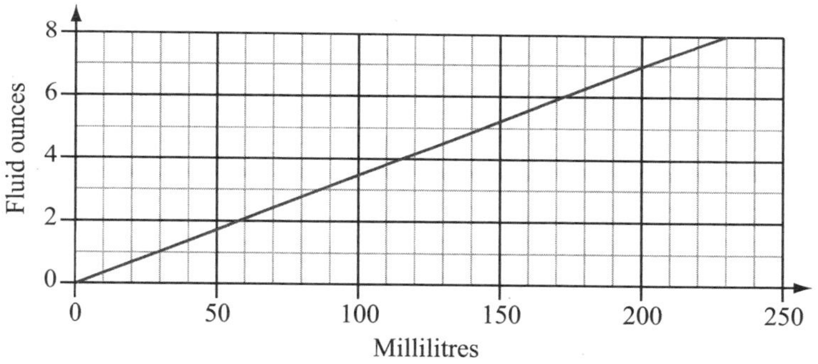

Use this information to work out how many fluid ounces would be needed for an American recipe that required one-and-a-half cups.

PS **5** Two parcel delivery companies use the following formulae for calculating delivery costs for packages:

LHD: £12.00 basic charge and £0.80 per kilometre
NTN: £10.00 basic charge and £1.00 per kilometre

LHD give a 10% discount if five or more orders are placed at the same time.
NTN give £2 off each delivery if five or more orders are placed at the same time.

Draw a conversion graph to illustrate this information.

A company needs to send five packages to five different places. The distances of each place from the company are 6, 8, 10, 12 and 15 kilometres.
Work out the cheapest way to send the packages.

E D C

9.2 Travel graphs

HOMEWORK 9B

D

FM 1 Joe was travelling in his car to meet his girlfriend. He set off from home at 9.00 pm, and stopped on the way for a break. This distance–time graph illustrates his journey.

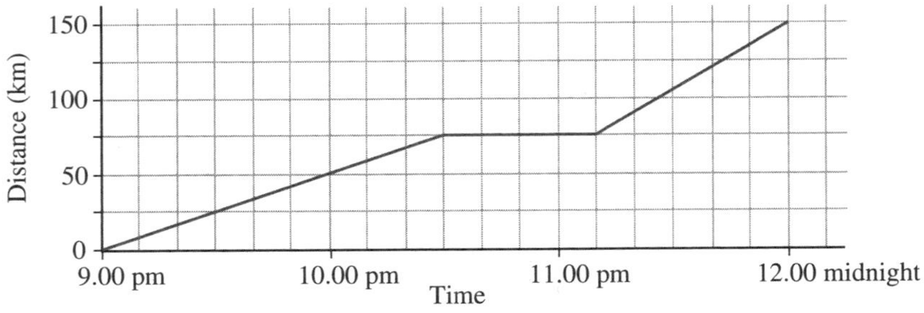

a At what time did he:

i stop for his break **ii** set off after his break **iii** get to his meeting place?

b At what average speed was he travelling:

i over the first hour **ii** over the last hour **iii** for the whole of his journey?

c Joe was 10 minutes late arriving. If he had stopped for half as long, would he have been on time?

FM 2 Jean set off in a taxi from Hellaby. The taxi then went on to pick up Jeans's parents. It then travelled further, dropping them all off at a shopping centre. The taxi went on a further 10 km to pick up another party and took them back to Hellaby. This distance–time graph illustrates the journey.

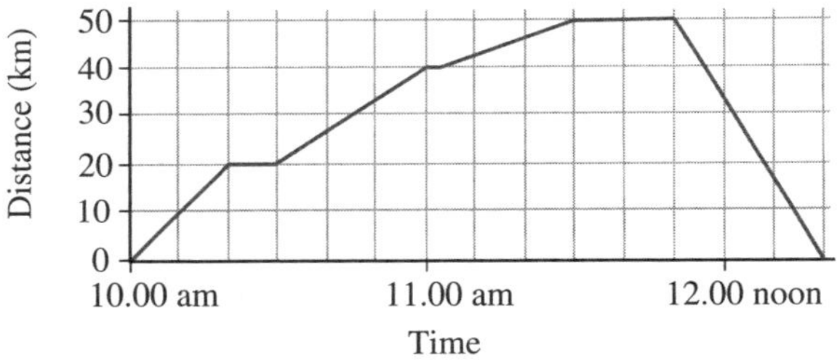

a How far from Hellaby did Jean's parents live?

b How far from Hellaby is the shopping centre?

c What was the average speed of the taxi while only Jean was in the taxi?

d What was the average speed of the taxi back to Hellaby?

FM 3 Grandad took his grandchildren out for a trip. They set off at 1.00 pm and travelled, for half an hour, away from Norwich at an average speed of 60 km/h. They stopped to look at the sea and have an ice cream. At two o'clock, they set off again, travelling for a quarter of an hour at a speed of 80 km/h. Then they stopped to play on the sand for half an hour. Grandad then drove the grandchildren back home at an average speed of 50 km/h.

Draw a travel graph to illustrate this story. Use a horizontal axis to represent time from 1.00 pm to 5.00 pm, and a vertical scale from 0 km to 60 km.

AU 4 A runner sets off at 8 am from point P to jog along a trail at a steady pace of 12 km per hour. One hour later, a cyclist sets off from P on the same trial at a steady pace of 24 km per hour. After 30 minutes, the cyclist gets a puncture which takes 30 minutes to fix. She then sets of at a steady pace of 24 km per hour.

At what time does the cyclist catch up with the runner? You may use a grid to help you solve this question.

HINTS AND TIPS

This question can be done by many methods, but doing a distance–time graph is the easiest. Mark a grid with a horizontal axis from 8 am to 12 pm and the vertical axis as distance from 0 to 40. Draw lines for both runner and cyclist. Remember that the cyclist doesn't start until 9 am.

PS 5 Three runners, A, B and C took part in a handicap race over 4 km. The graph shows how each runner ran in the race.

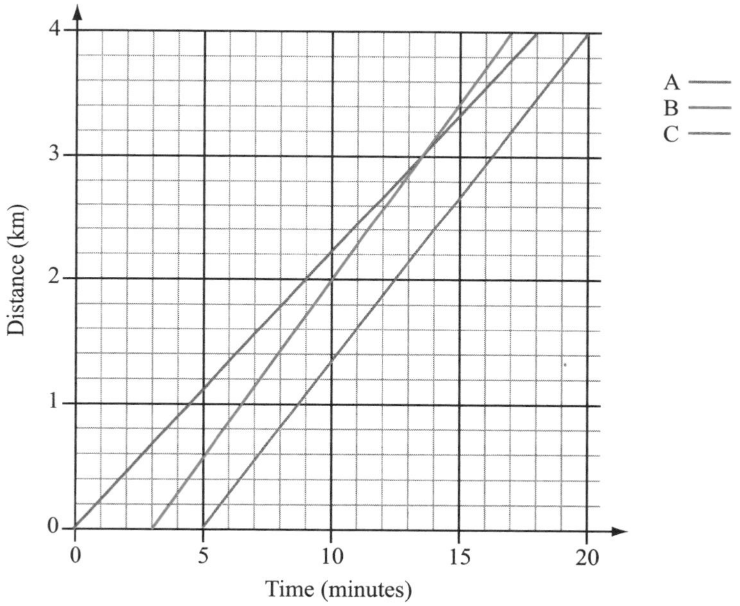

Runner A had a zero handicap and finished the race on 18 minutes.

Runner B had a.3-minute handicap and finished the race on 17 minutes.

a **i** What was runner C's handicap?

ii On what time from the start did runner C finish?

b Who ran the distance in the fastest actual time?

c The following week, the runners do the same race again. Assuming that they run at the same pace, what handicaps should all the runners have so that they finish at the same time?

9.3 Flow diagrams and graphs

HOMEWORK 9C

1 Draw the graph of $y = x + 1$

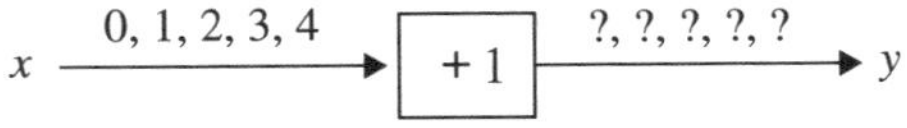

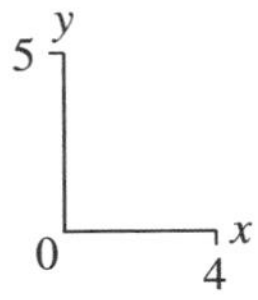

x	0	1	2	3	4
y					

2 Draw the graph of $y = 2x + 1$

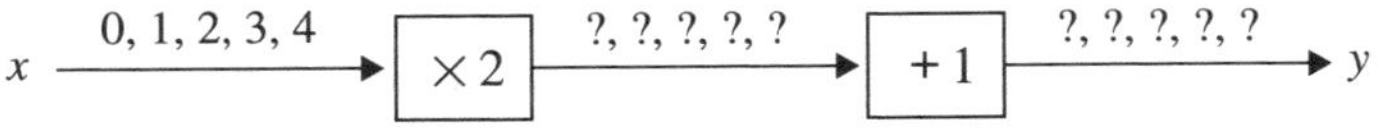

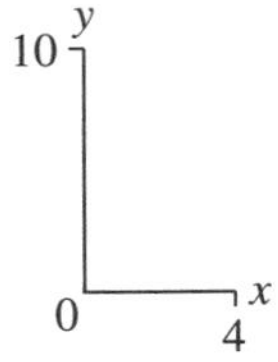

x	0	1	2	3	4
y					

3 Draw the graph of $y = 3x + 1$

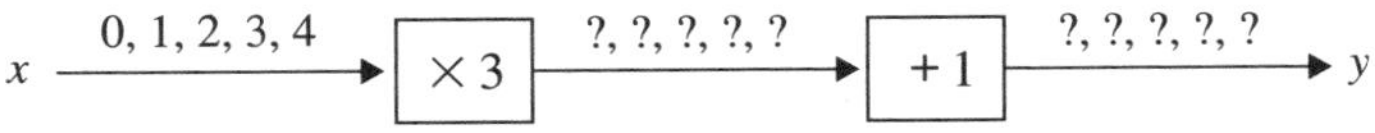

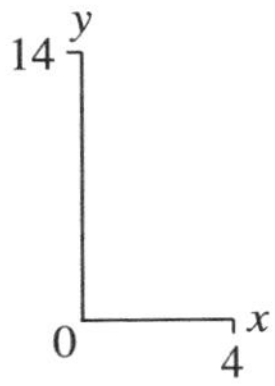

x	0	1	2	3	4
y					

4 Draw the graph of $y = x - 1$

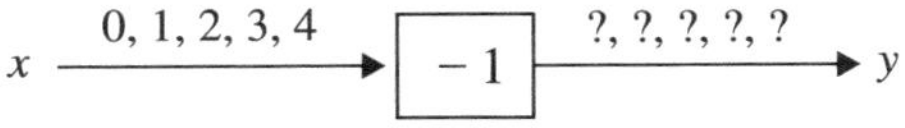

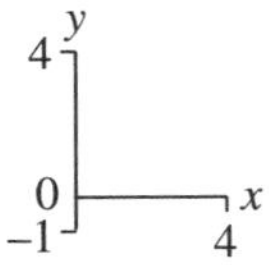

x	0	1	2	3	4
y					

5 **a** Draw the graphs of $y = x - 2$ and $y = 2x - 1$ on the same grid.
b Where do the graphs cross?

6 **a** Draw the graphs of $y = 2x$ and $y = x + 2$ on the same grid.
b Where do the graphs cross?

PS 7 This flow diagram connects two variables P and Q.

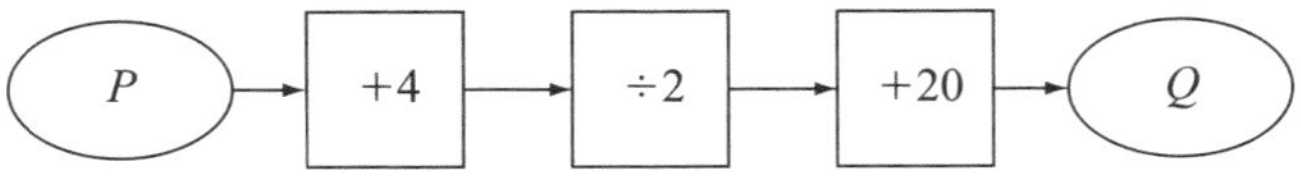

This graph also connects the variables P and Q.
Copy the graph and fill in the missing values on the P axis.

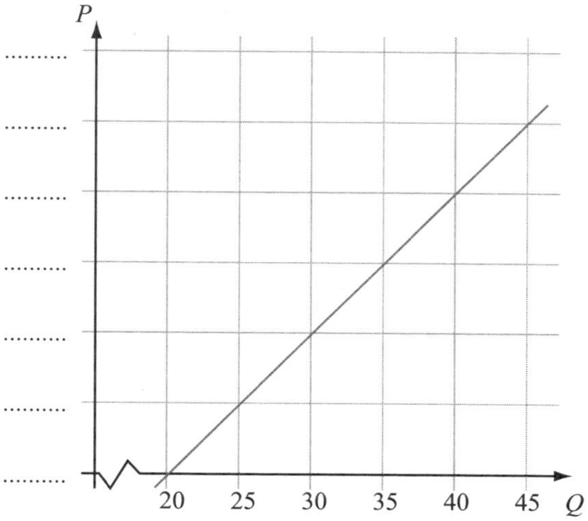

FM 8 A theatre charges £10.00 for an adult ticket and £7.50 for a child ticket.
No children are allowed to go to a performance without at least one adult present.
To work out the cost of various combinations, they use a wall chart or a flow diagram.

a Use the flow chart to work out the cost of three adults and two children.

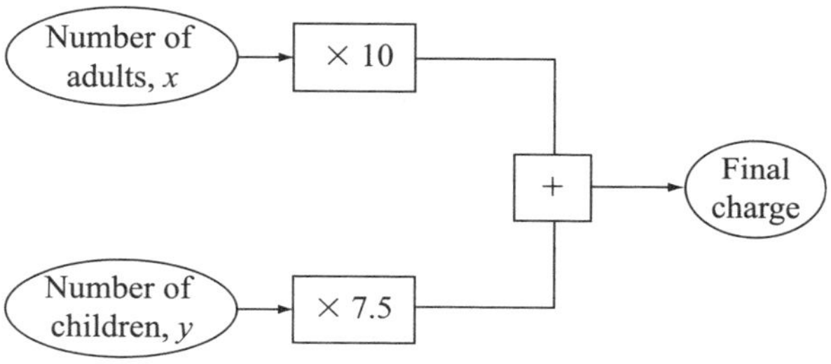

b Draw a chart to show the costs of tickets for up to five adults and four children. Use the flow diagram to complete the chart.

c A group paid £30.00. Can you say for sure how many adults and/or children there were in the party?

AU 9 A teacher reads out the following think-of-a-number problem:
'I am thinking of a number, I divide it by 2 and then subtract 1.'

a Represent this using a flow diagram.

b If the input is x and the output is y, write down a relationship between x and y.

c Draw a graph for x values from 0 to 6.

d Explain how you could use the graph to find the number someone thought of if their final answer was 1.5.

9.4 Linear graphs

HOMEWORK 9D

Draw the graph for each of the equations given.

Follow these hints.

- Use the highest and smallest values of x given as your range.
- When the first part of the function is a division, pick x-values that divide exactly to avoid fractions.
- Always label your graphs. This is particularly important when you are drawing two graphs on the same set of axes.
- Create a table of values. You will often have to complete these in your examinations.

D

1 Draw the graph of $y = 2x + 3$ for x-values from 0 to 5 ($0 \leqslant x \leqslant 5$)

2 Draw the graph of $y = 3x - 1$ $\quad (0 \leqslant x \leqslant 5)$

3 Draw the graph of $y = \frac{x}{2} - 2$ $\quad (0 \leqslant x \leqslant 12)$

4 Draw the graph of $y = 2x + 1$ $\quad (-2 \leqslant x \leqslant 2)$

5 Draw the graph of $y = \frac{x}{2} + 5$ $\quad (-6 \leqslant x \leqslant 6)$

6 **a** On the same set of axes, draw the graphs of $y = 3x - 1$ and $y = 2x + 3$ $\quad (0 \leqslant x \leqslant 5)$

b Where do the two graphs cross?

7 **a** On the same axes, draw the graphs of $y = 4x - 3$ and $y = 3x + 2$ $\quad (0 \leqslant x \leqslant 6)$

b Where do the two graphs cross?

8 **a** On the same axes, draw the graphs of

$y = \frac{x}{2} + 1$ and $y = \frac{x}{3} + 2$ $\quad (0 \leqslant x \leqslant 12)$

b Where do the two graphs cross?

9 **a** On the same axes, draw the graphs of $y = 2x + 3$ and $y = 2x - 1$ $\quad (0 \leqslant x \leqslant 4)$

b Do the graphs cross? If not, why not?

10 **a** Copy and complete the table to draw the graph of $x + y = 6$ $\quad (0 \leqslant x \leqslant 6)$

b Now draw the graph of $x + y = 3$ $\quad (0 \leqslant x \leqslant 6)$

x	0	1	2	3	4	5	6
y							

FM 11 CityCabs uses this formula to work out the cost of a journey of k kilometres:
$C = 2.5 + k$
TownCars uses this formula to work out the cost of a journey of k kilometres:
$C = 2 + 1.25k$

a Draw a grid of distance (k) against cost (C) like the one below. Represent these formulae as lines on your grid.

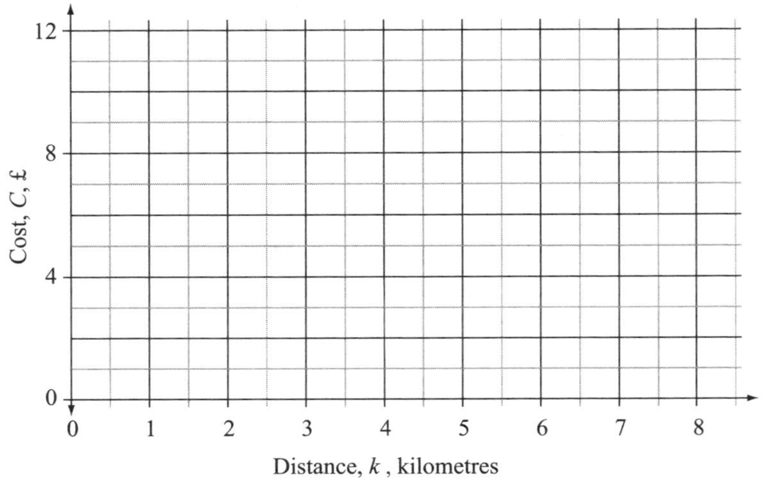

b At what length of journey do CityCabs and TownCars charge the same amount?

C

AU 12 The line $x + y = 5$ is drawn on the grid below.

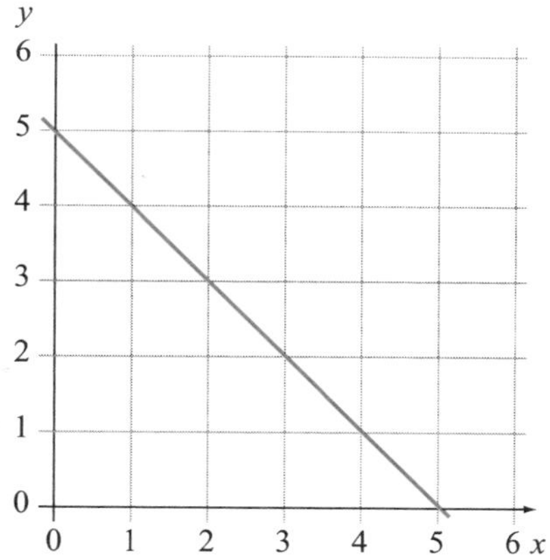

Choose values for a and b and draw the line $x = a$ and $y = b$ so that the area between the three lines is 4.5 square units.

PS 13 The two graphs shown show y against x and y against z.

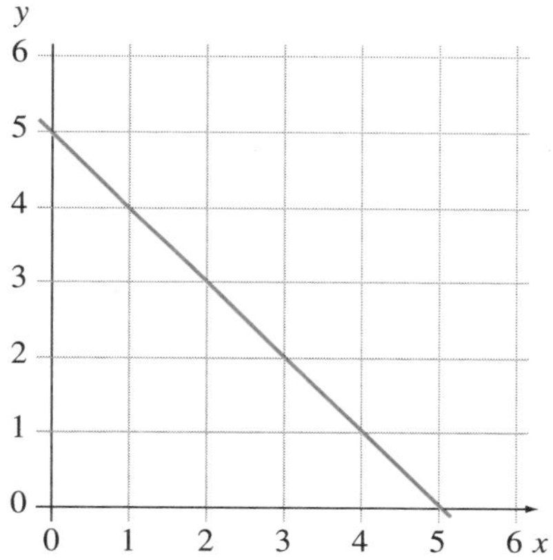

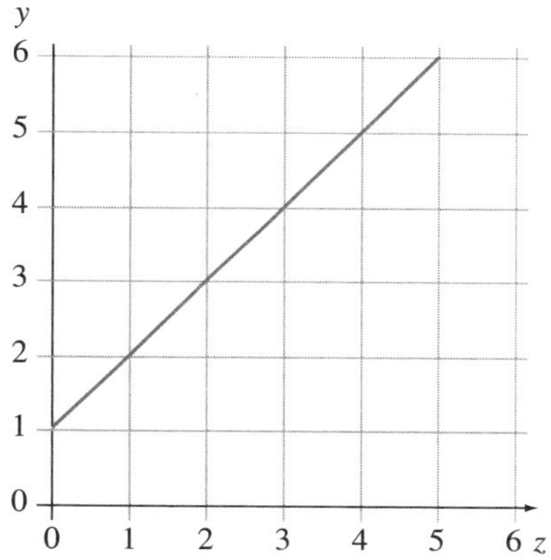

Draw a grid to show the graph of x against z.

HOMEWORK 9E

C

1 Find the gradient of each of these lines.

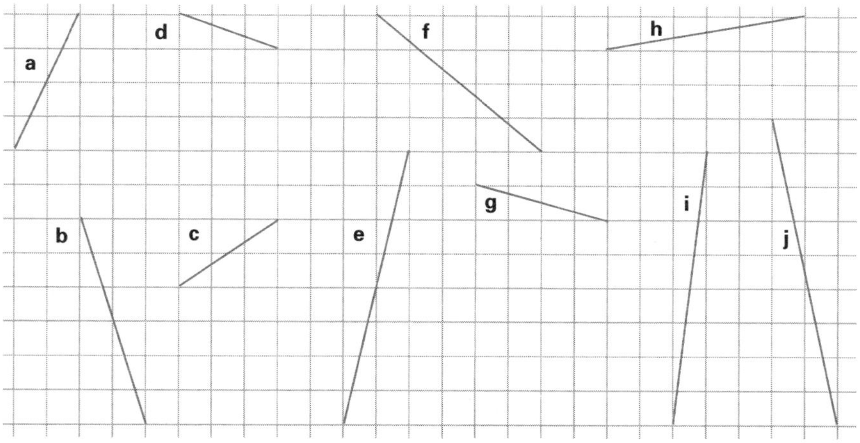

2 Draw lines with gradients of:

a 3 **b** $\frac{1}{2}$ **c** –1

d 8 **e** $\frac{3}{4}$ **f** $-\frac{1}{3}$

3 **a** Draw a pair of axes with both x and y showing from –10 to 10.

b Draw on the grid lines with the following gradients; start each line at the origin. Clearly label each line.

i $\frac{1}{2}$ **ii** 1 **iii** 2

iv 4 **v** –4 **vi** –2

vii –1 **viii** $-\frac{1}{2}$

c Describe the symmetries of your diagram.

HINTS AND TIPS

The origin is the point where the x and y axes cross.

4 This graph shows the journey of a car from London to Brighton and back again. The car leaves at 8 am and returns at 3 pm.

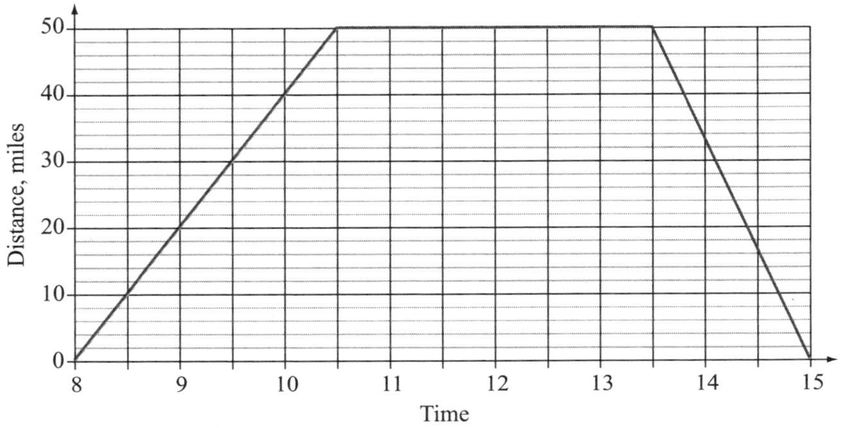

a How long does the car stop for in Brighton?

b Was the car travelling faster on the way to Brighton or on the way back to London? Explain how you can tell this from the graph.

FM PS **5** The diagram shows the safe position for a ladder. Use a grid like the one below and a protractor to work out the approximate safe angle between the ladder and the ground, marked x on the diagram.

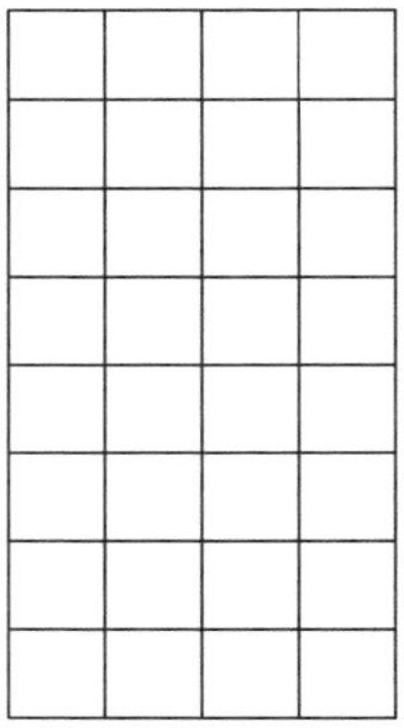

AU 6 A class is asked to predict the y-value for an x-value of 20 for this line.

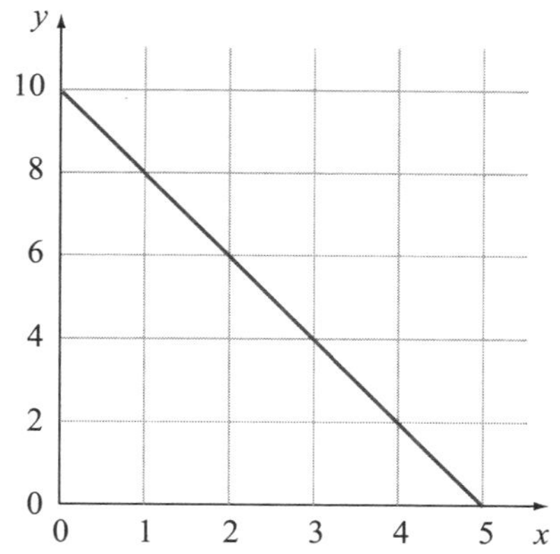

Steph says: 'The gradient is –1, so the line is $y = -x + 10$. When $x = 20$, $y = -10$.'
Steph is wrong.
Explain why and work out the correct y-value when $x = 20$.

Functional Maths Activity

Driving in the United States

a Petrol is sold in gallons in the United States and in litres in the United Kingdom. Until recently, petrol was sold in Imperial gallons in the United Kingdom. These two graphs show the conversions between United States gallons and Imperial gallons and between Imperial gallons and litres.

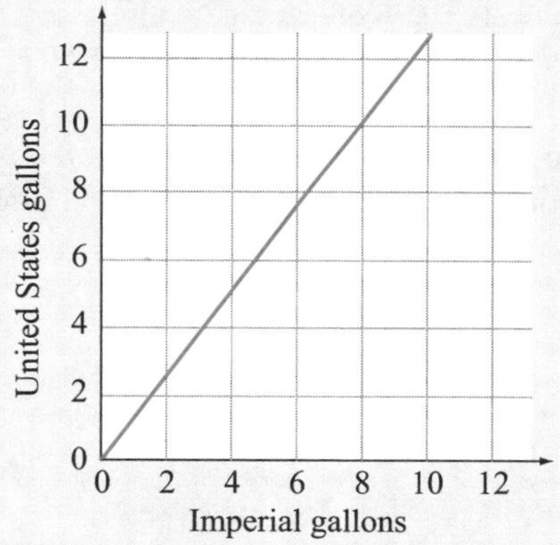

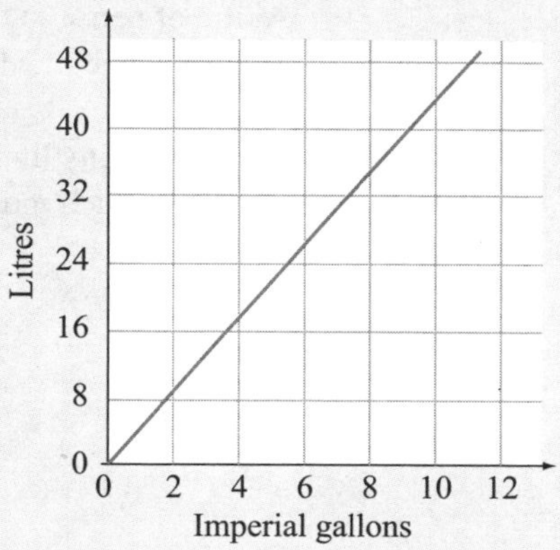

Approximately how many litres are there in a US gallon?

b This is an American advert for a car.

Functional Maths Activity (continued)

This is a map of the highway distances between four cities in the United States.

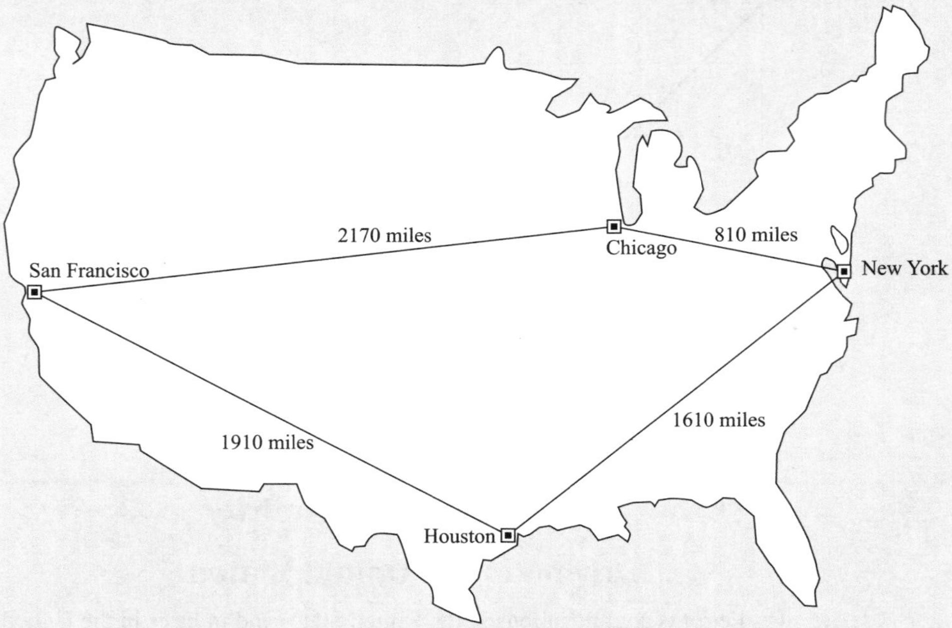

Jeff goes on a road trip from New York to Chicago, to San Francisco, to Houston and back to New York.

A US gallon of petrol costs \$2.12 on average.

A litre of petrol in the UK costs £0.96 on average.

The exchange rate between pounds and dollars is £1 = \$1.60

Work out:

i How many litres of fuel would be used on this journey.

ii How much more it would cost at UK prices than at US prices for the fuel.

10 Geometry and measures: Angles

10.1 Measuring and drawing angles

HOMEWORK 10A

F

1 Use a protractor to find the size of each marked angle.

a

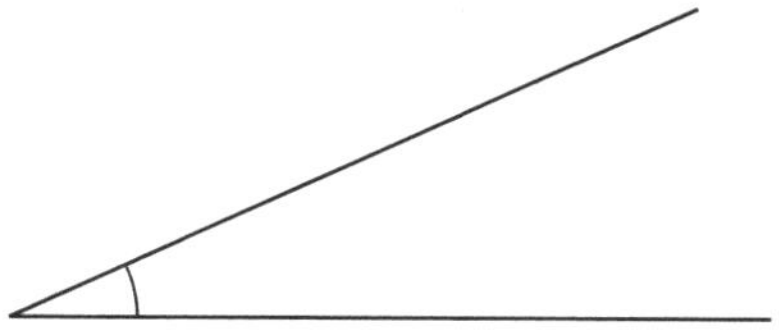

b

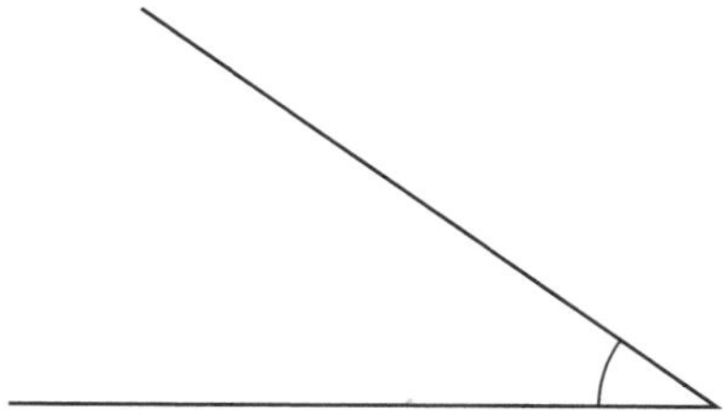

c

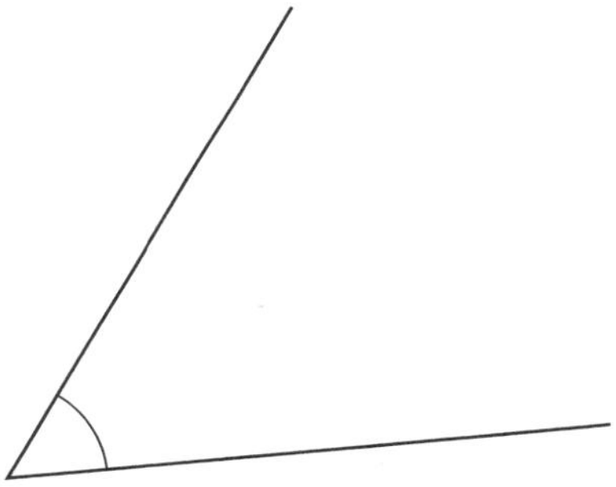

d

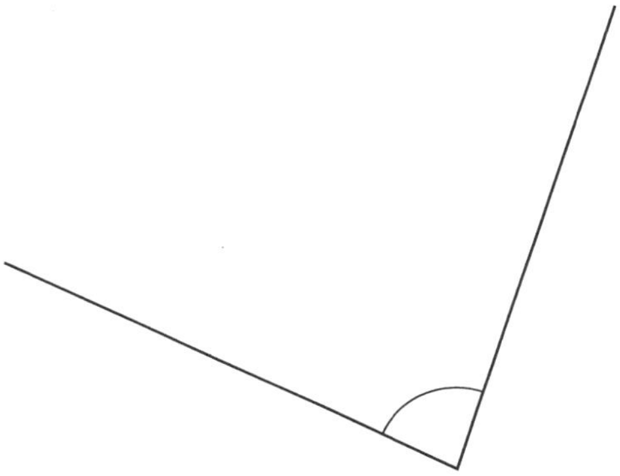

e

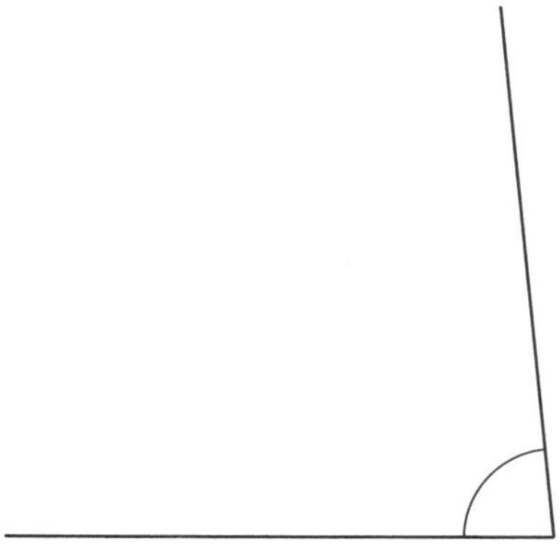

f

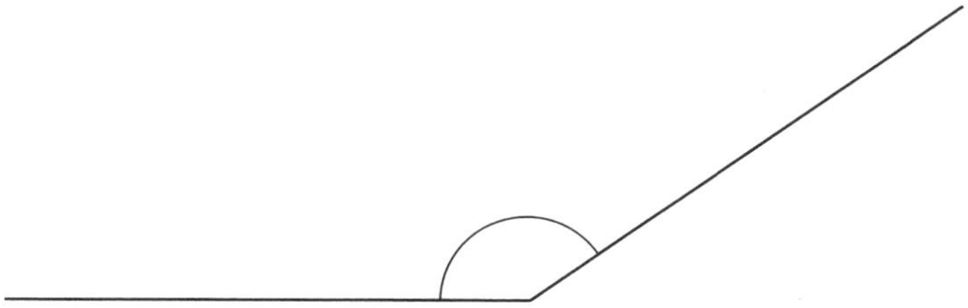

g

h

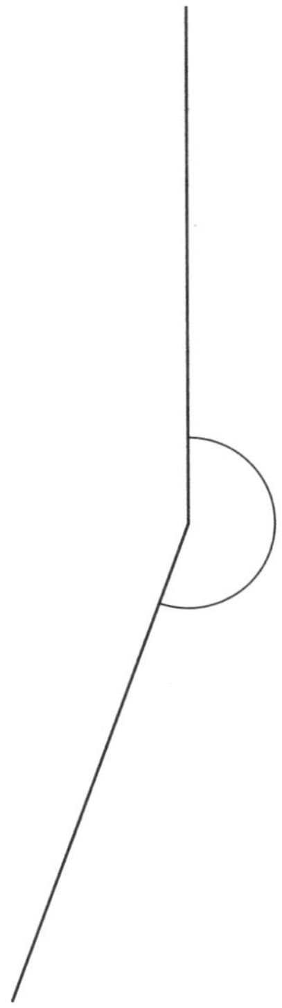

2 Draw angles of the following sizes.

a 30° **b** 42° **c** 55° **d** 68°
e 75° **f** 140° **g** 164° **h** 245°

3 **a** Draw any three acute angles.
b Estimate their sizes. Record your results.
c Measure the angles. Record your results.
d Work out the difference between your estimate and your measurement for each angle.

4 Baden is using his compass and map to measure the angle between the North line and the summit of a mountain.

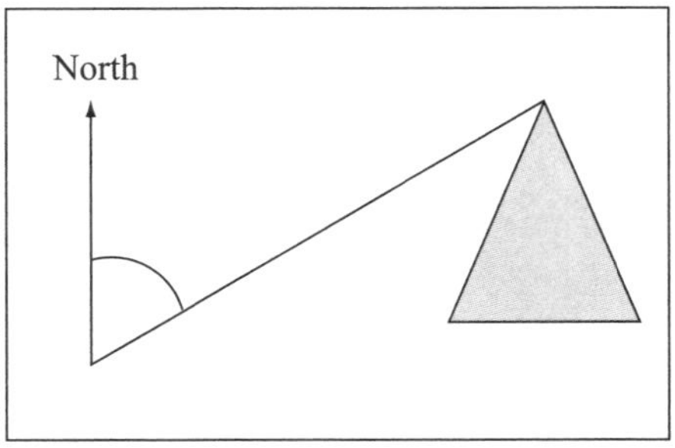

What is the size of the angle?

AU 5 Is angle ABC bigger than angle XYZ?

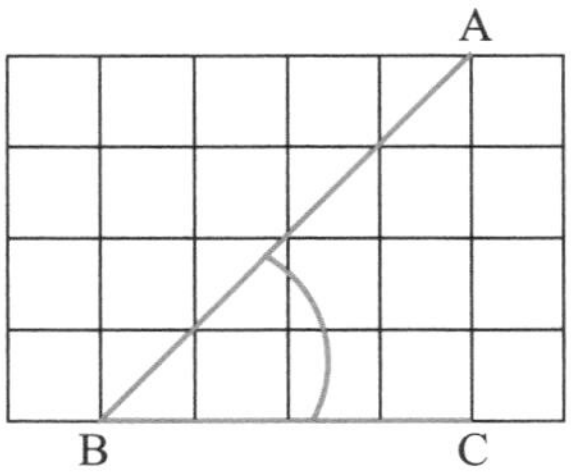

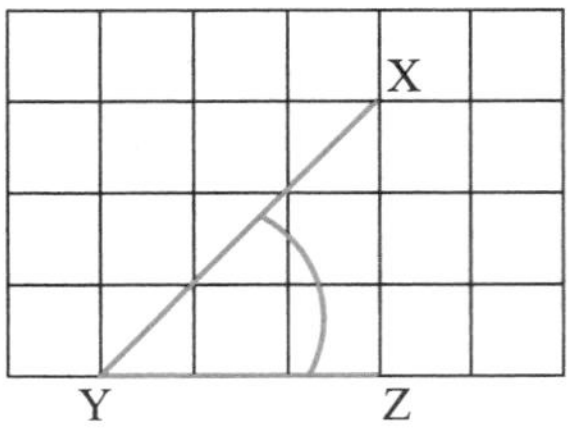

Give a reason for your answer.

AU 6 Which angle is the odd one out?
Give a reason for your answer.

a

b

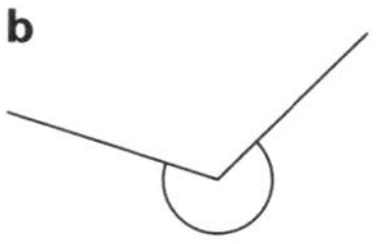

c

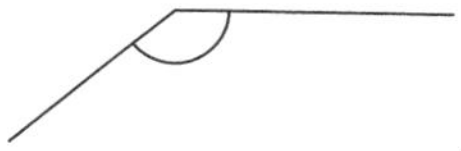

d

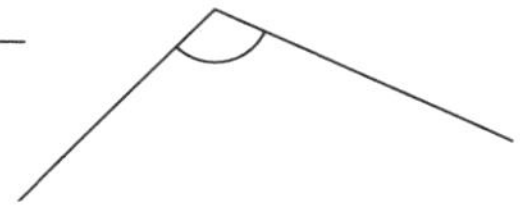

PS 7 An acute angle is half the size of an obtuse angle.
Write down a possible size for the acute angle.

FM 8 When plumbers want to change the direction of a water pipe, they use a short section of bent pipe called an elbow. The most common types are a 90 degree elbow or a 45 degree elbow. Sketch what you think they look like.

FM 9 An acute angle is half the size of an obtuse angle.
Write down a possible size for the acute angle.

10.2 Angle facts

HOMEWORK 10B

Example Find the value of x in the diagram.

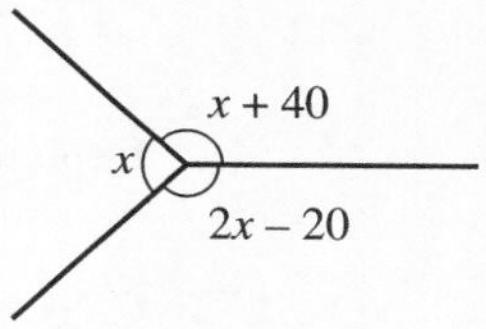

These angles are around a point and add up to 360°.

So $x + x + 40 + 2x - 20 = 360°$

$4x + 20 = 360°$

$4x = 340°$

$x = 85°$

1 Calculate the size of the angle marked x in each of these examples.

a

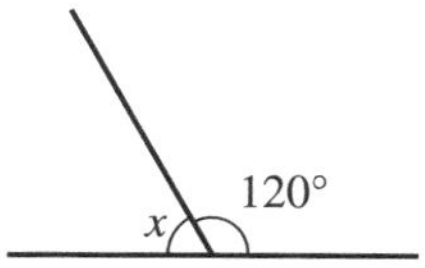

b

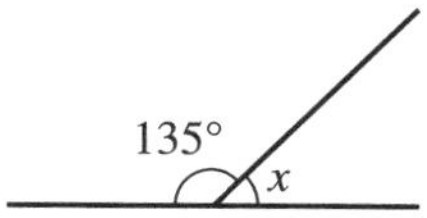

c

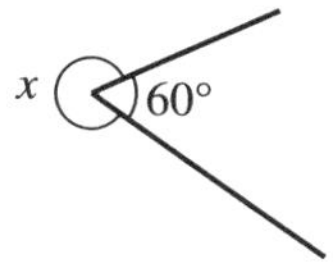

d

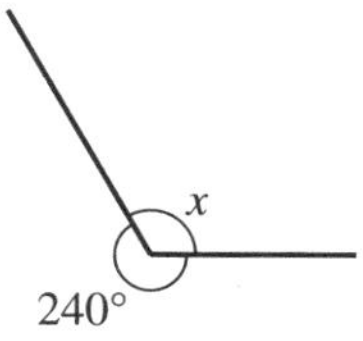

e

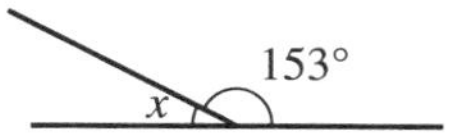

f

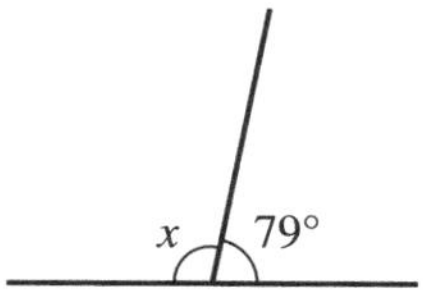

g

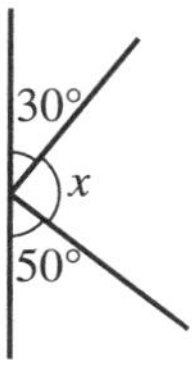

h

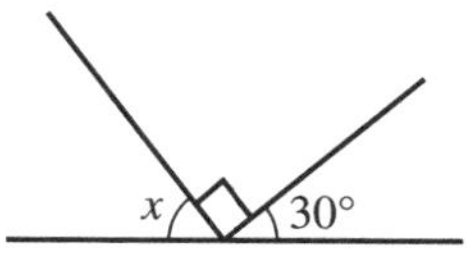

i

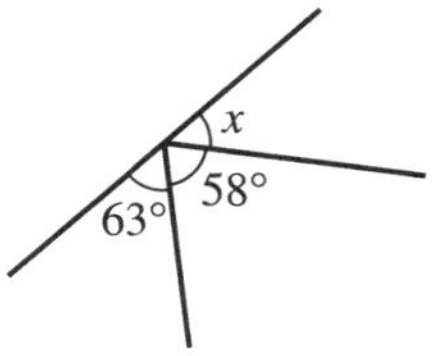

F

j

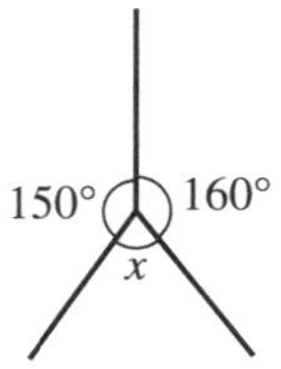

k

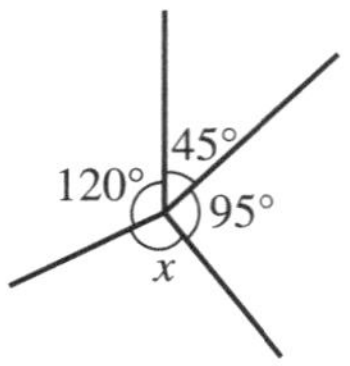

l

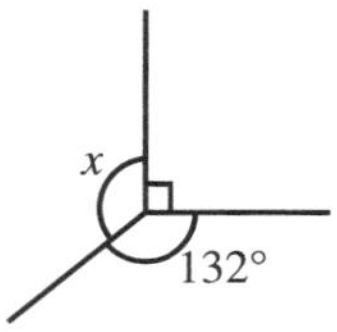

m

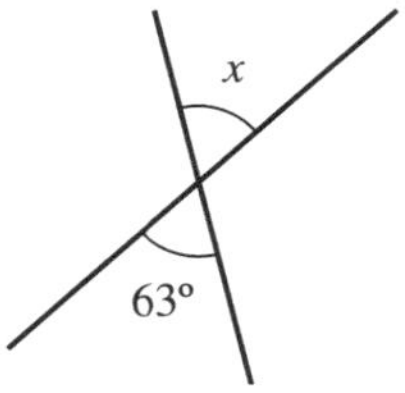

n

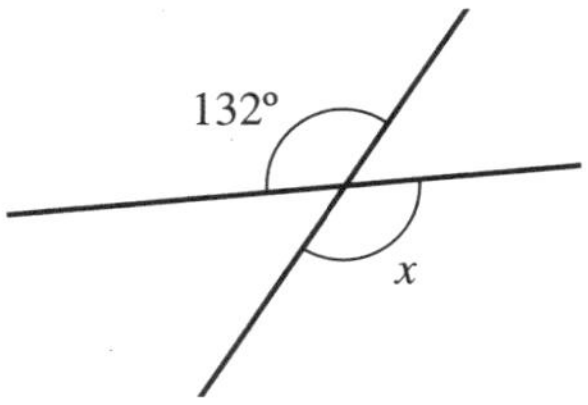

AU 2 Will these three angles fit together to make a straight line?

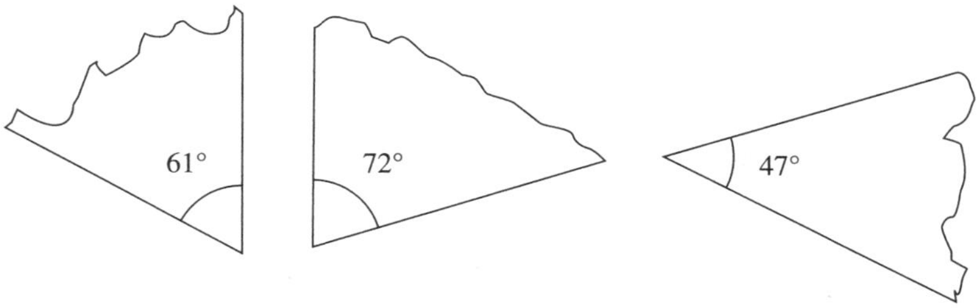

Explain your answer.

E

3 Calculate the value of x in each of these examples.

a

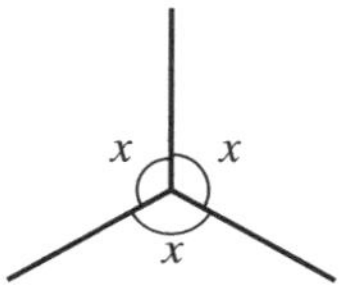

b

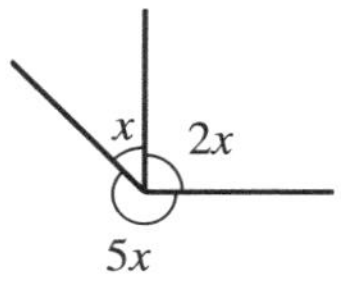

c

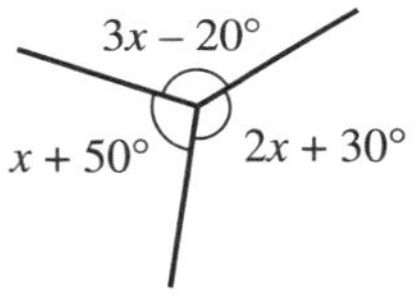

4 Calculate the value of x in each of these examples.

a

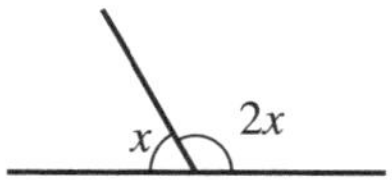

b

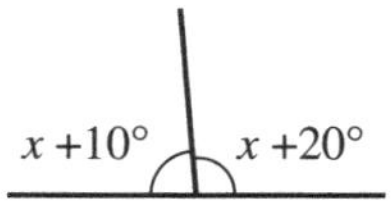

c

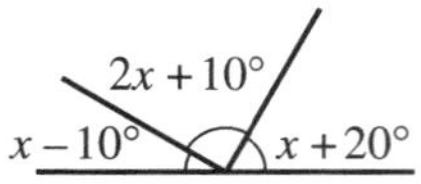

5 Calculate the value of x first and then find the size of angle y in each of these examples.

a

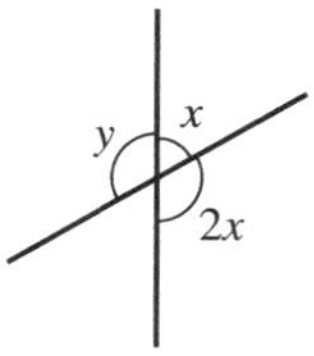

b

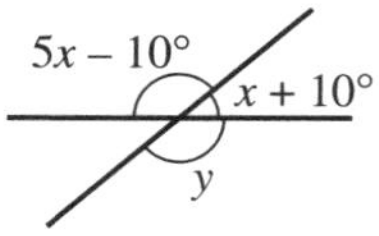

c

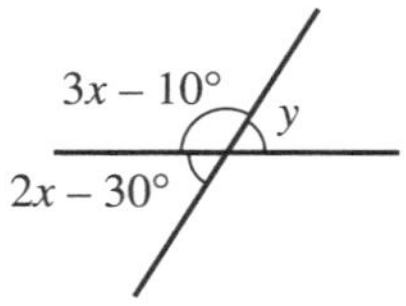

FM 6 These paving stones are in the shape of regular hexagons.
Explain why they fit together without leaving any gaps.

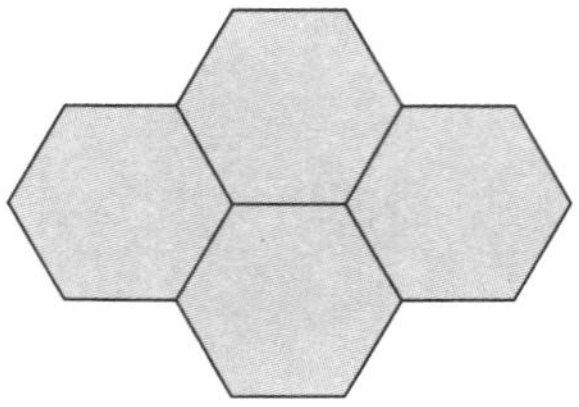

HINTS AND TIPS

All the angles inside a regular hexagon are 120°.

PS 7 Angle BXC is three times the size of angle AXB and angle AXC is five times the size of angle AXB.
Work out the size of the three angles.

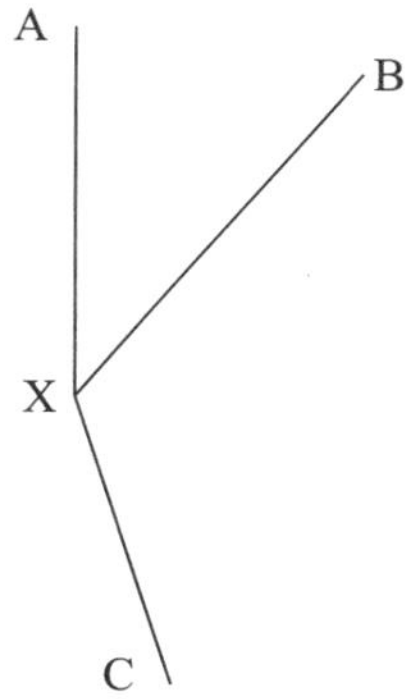

10.3 Angles in a triangle

HOMEWORK 10C

1 Find the size of the angle marked with a letter in each of these triangles.

a

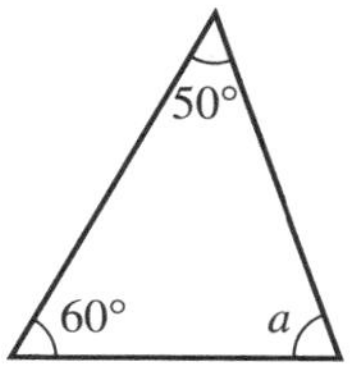

b

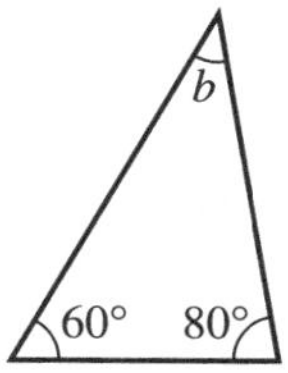

c

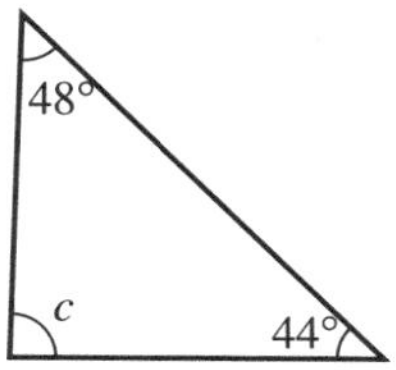

d

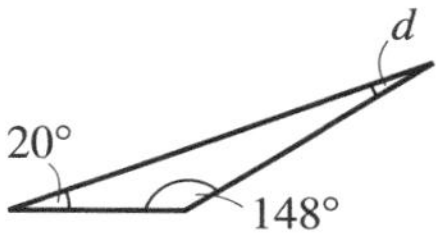

e

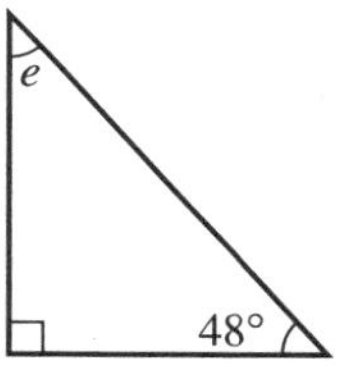

f

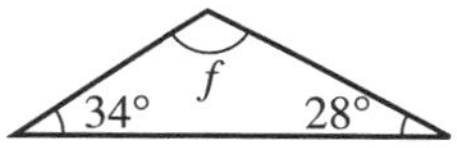

AU 2 State whether each of these sets of angles are the three angles of a triangle? Explain your answers.

a 15°, 85° and 80° **b** 40°, 60° and 90° **c** 25°, 25° and 110°
d 40°, 40° and 100° **e** 32°, 37° and 111° **f** 61°, 59° and 70°

3 The three interior angles of a triangle are given in each case. Find the angle indicated by a letter.

a 40°, 70° and a° **b** 60°, 60° and b° **c** 80°, 90° and c°
d 65°, 72° and d° **e** 130°, 45° and e° **f** 112°, 27° and f°

4 In a triangle all the interior angles are the same.

a What size is each angle?
b What is the special name of this triangle?
c What is special about the sides of this triangle?

5 In the triangle on the right, two of the angles are the same.

a Work out the size of the lettered angles.
b What is the special name of this triangle?
c What is special about the sides AB and AC of this triangle?

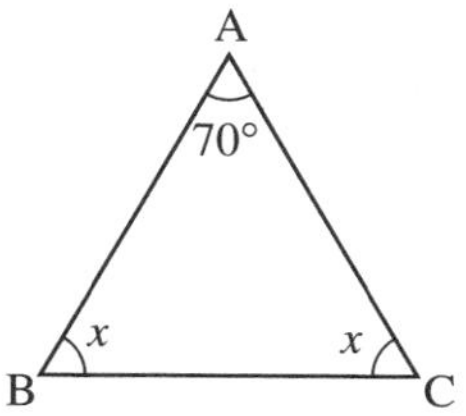

E

6 In the triangle on the right, the size of the angle at C is twice the size of the angle at A. Work out the size of the lettered angles.

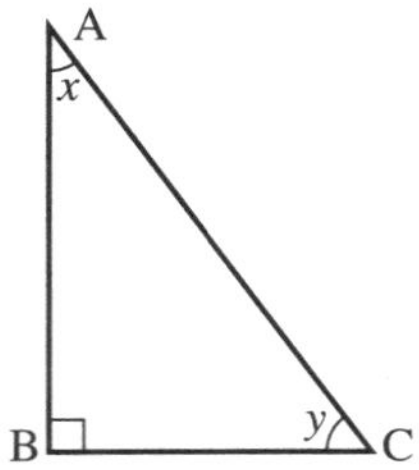

7 Find the size of the angle marked with a letter in each of the diagrams.

a

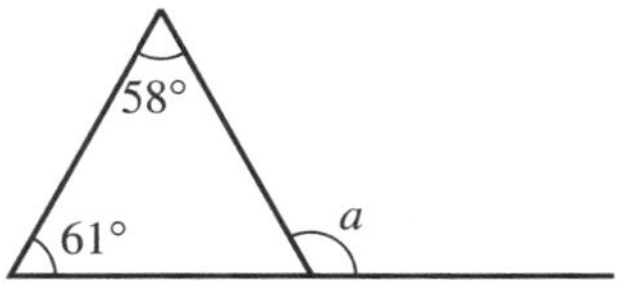

b

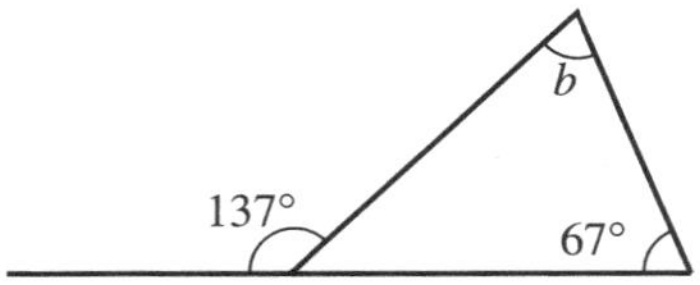

FM 8 The diagram shows a guy rope attached to a mast of a marquee.

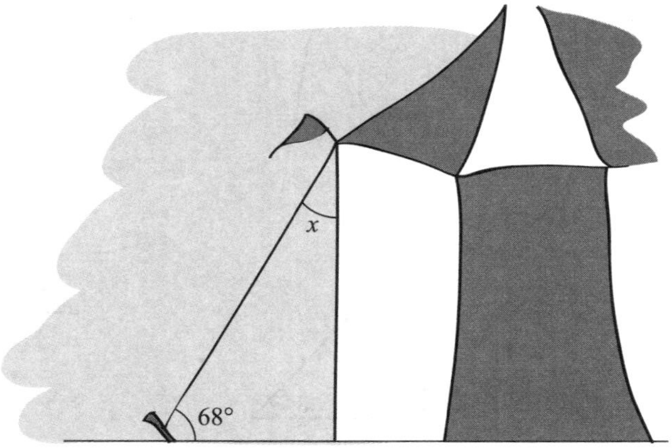

Find the size of angle x marked on the diagram.

AU 9 Here are five statements about triangles. Some are true and some are false.

1. A triangle can have three acute angles.
2. A triangle can have two acute angles and one obtuse angle.
3. A triangle can have one acute angle and two obtuse angles.
4. A triangle can have two acute angles and one right-angle.
5. A triangle can have one acute angle and two right-angles.

If a statement is true, draw a sketch of a triangle.
If a statement is false, explain why.

AU 10

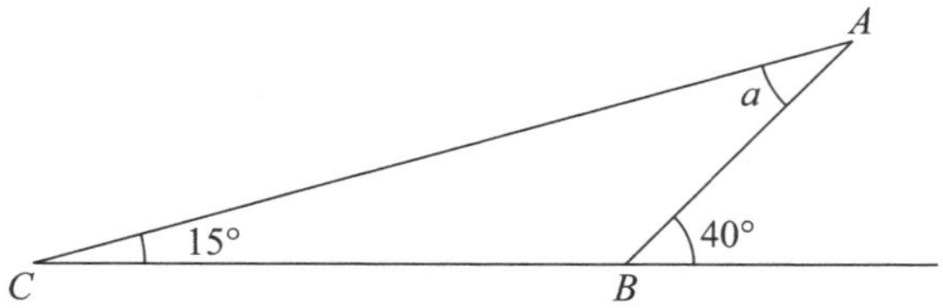

Explain why angle a is 25 degrees.

AU 11 A town planner has drawn this diagram to show three paths in a park, but they have missed out the angle marked x.

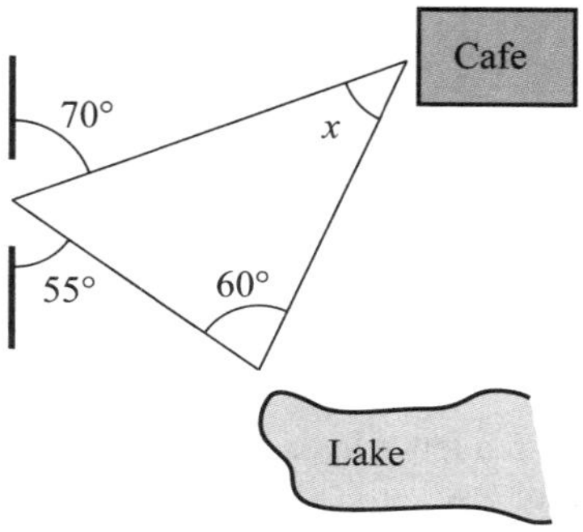

Work out the value of x.

10.4 Angles in a polygon

HOMEWORK 10D

1 Find the size of the angle marked with a letter in each of these quadrilaterals.

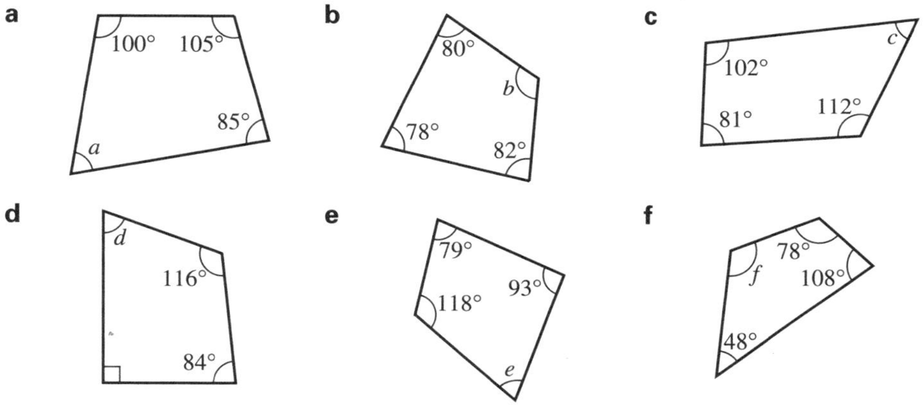

AU 2 State whether each of these sets of angles are the four interior angles of a quadrilateral? Explain your answers.

a 125°, 65°, 70° and 90°
b 100°, 60°, 70° and 130°
c 85°, 95°, 85° and 95°
d 120°, 120°, 70° and 60°
e 112°, 68°, 32° and 138°
f 151°, 102°, 73° and 34°

3 Three interior angles of a quadrilateral are given. Find the fourth angle indicated by a letter.

a 110°, 90°, 70° and a°
b 100°, 100°, 80° and b°
c 60°, 60°, 160° and c°
d 135°, 122°, 57° and d°
e 125°, 142°, 63° and e°
f 102°, 72°, 49° and f°

4 For the quadrilateral on the right:

a find the size of angle x.
b What type of angle is x?
c What is the special name of a quadrilateral like this?

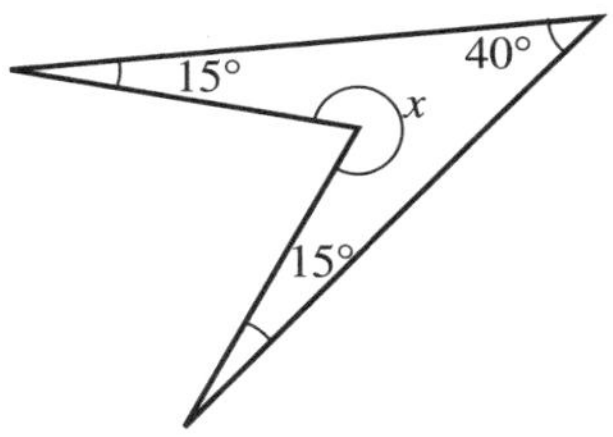

D

AU **5** **a** Draw a diagram to explain why the sum of the interior angles of any pentagon is 540°.

b Find the size of the angle x in the pentagon.

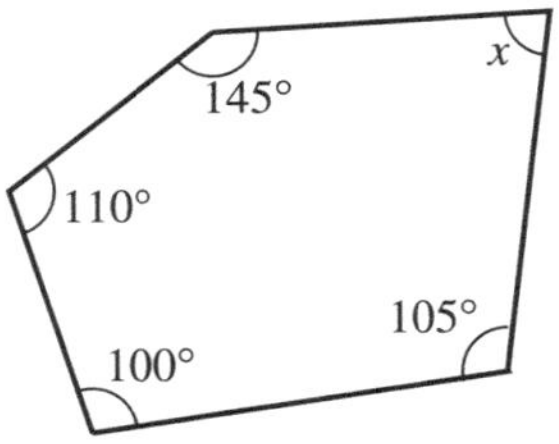

6 Calculate the size of the angle marked with a letter in each of the polygons below.

a

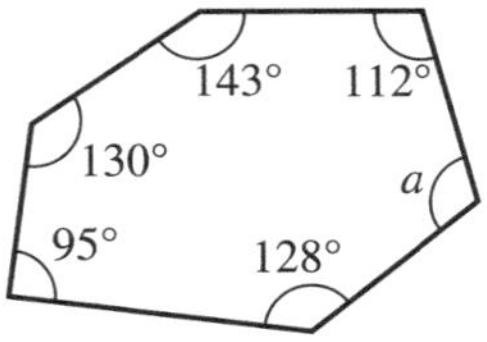

b

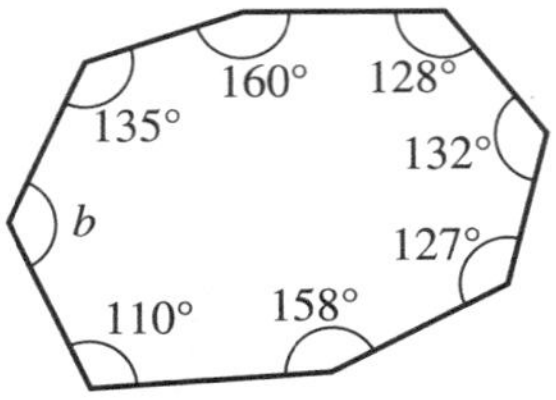

FM **7** Jamal is cutting metal from a rectangular sheet to make this sign.

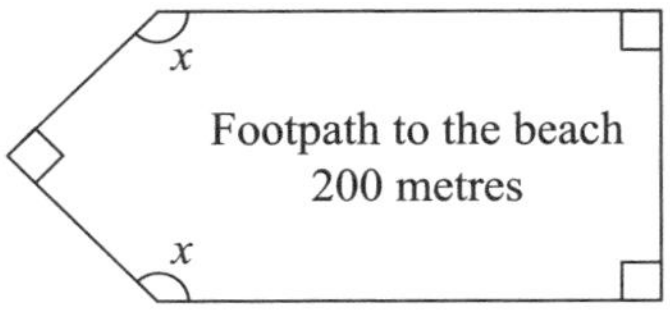

He needs to cut the two angles marked x accurately. How big is each one?

PS **8** Find the value of x in the diagram.

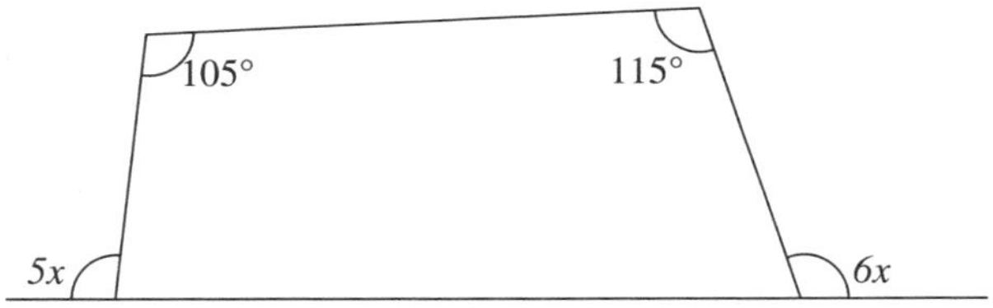

AU **9** The diagram shows a quadrilateral.

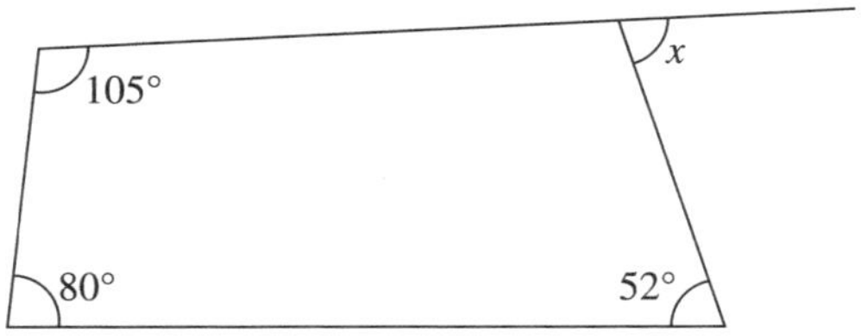

Paul says that the size of angle x is 52°

Explain why Paul is wrong.

Work out the correct value for x.

10.5 Regular polygons

HOMEWORK 10E

1 For each regular polygon below, find the interior angle x and the exterior angle y.

a

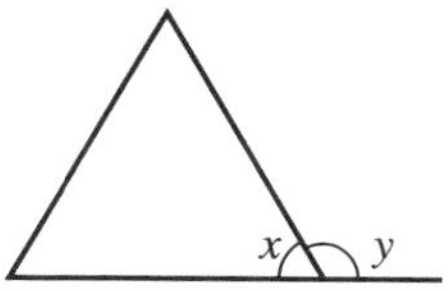

b

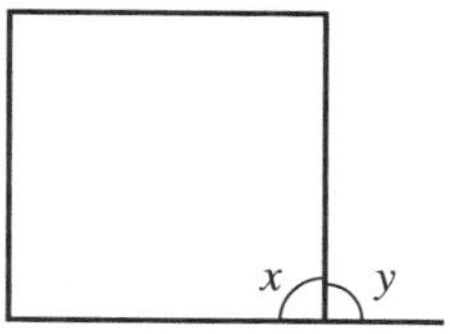

c

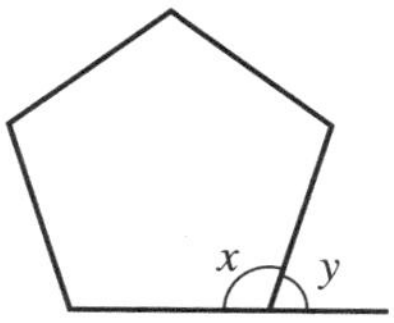

d

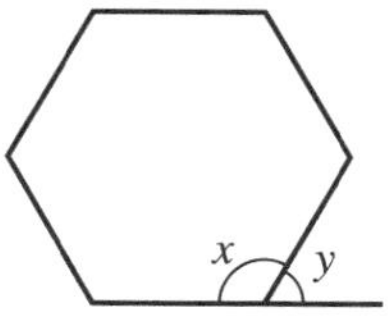

e

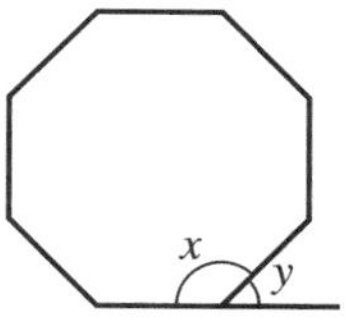

2 Find the number of sides of the regular polygon with an exterior angle of:
a 20° **b** 30° **c** 18° **d** 4°.

3 Find the number of sides of the regular polygon with an interior angle of:
a 135° **b** 165° **c** 170° **d** 156°.

4 What is the name of the regular polygon whose interior angle is treble its exterior angle?

FM 5 Four regular octagonal tiles of the same size are put together to make a floor tiling pattern.

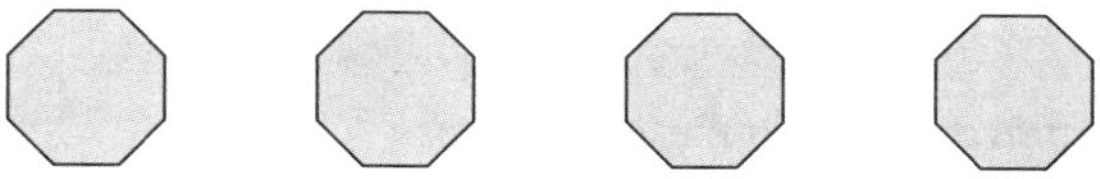

What is the shape of the tile that is required to fill the gap?

PS 6 ABCDE is a regular pentagon.

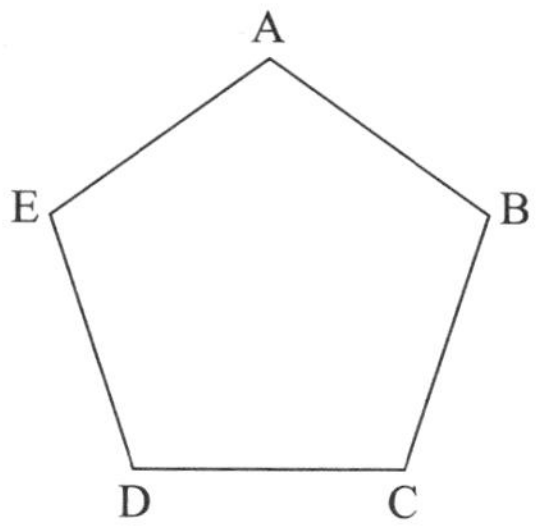

Work out the size of angle ADE.
Give reasons for your answer.

AU 7 Which of the following statements are true for a regular hexagon?

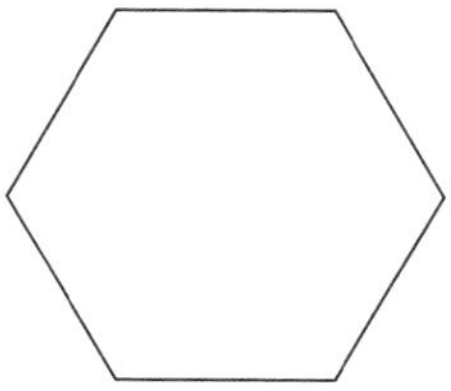

1. The size of each interior angle is 60°
2. The size of each interior angle is 120°
3. The size of each exterior angle is 60°
4. The size of each exterior angle is 240°

10.6 Parallel lines

HOMEWORK 10F

D

1 State the size of the lettered angles in each diagram.

a

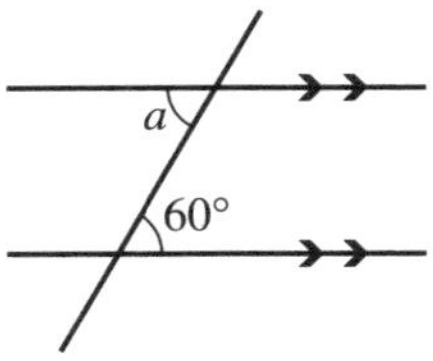

b

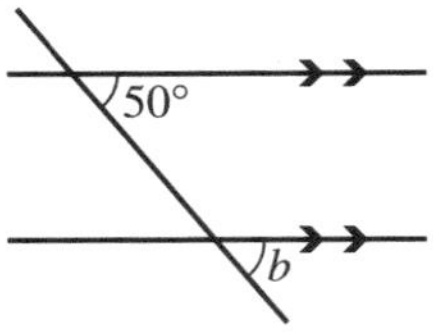

c

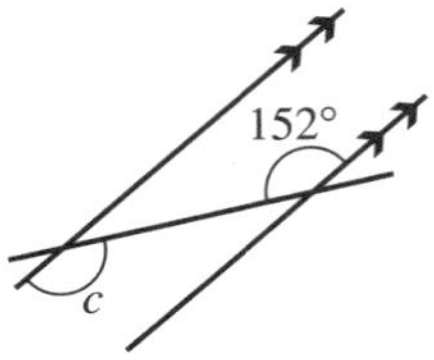

d

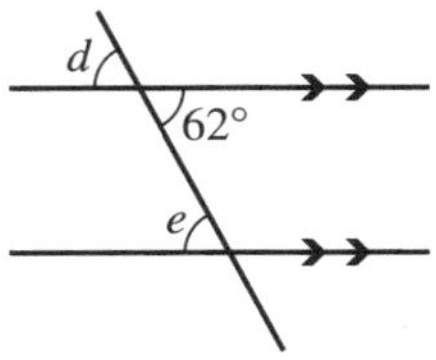

e

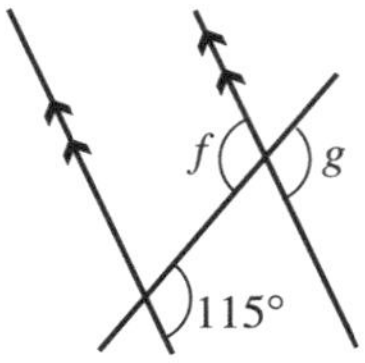

f

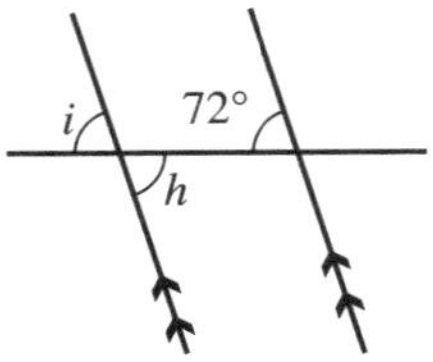

2 State the size of the lettered angles in each diagram.

a

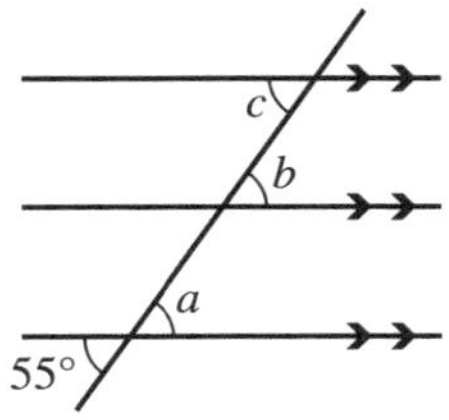

b

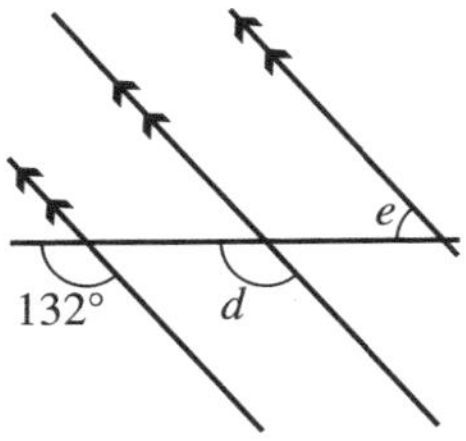

c

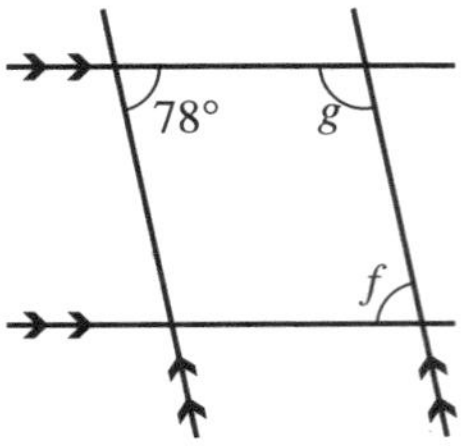

3 State the size of the lettered angles in these diagrams.

a

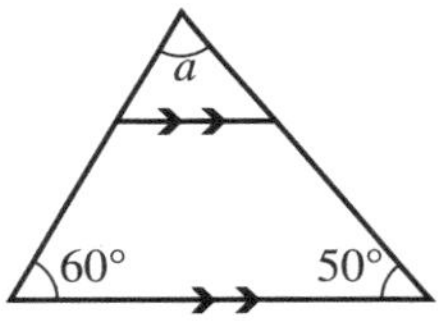

b

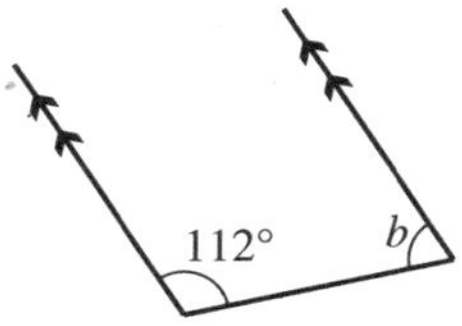

4 Find the values of x and y in these diagrams.

a

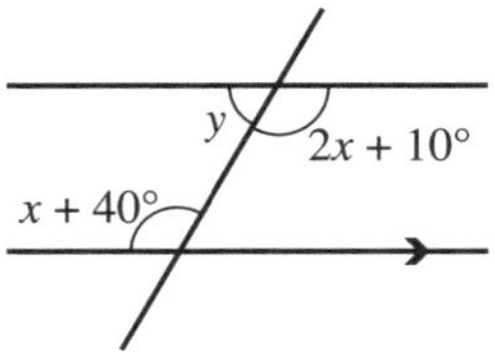

b

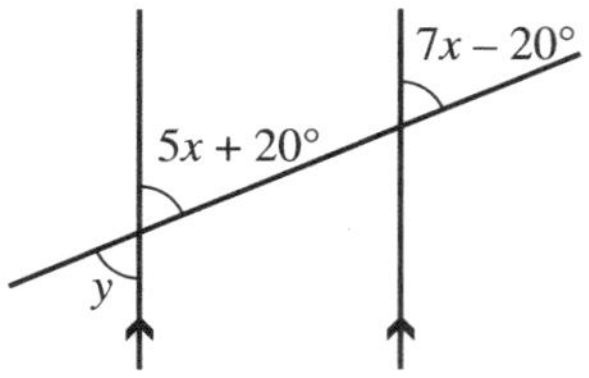

5 ABC is an isosceles triangle with angle ABC 52°.
XY is parallel to BC.

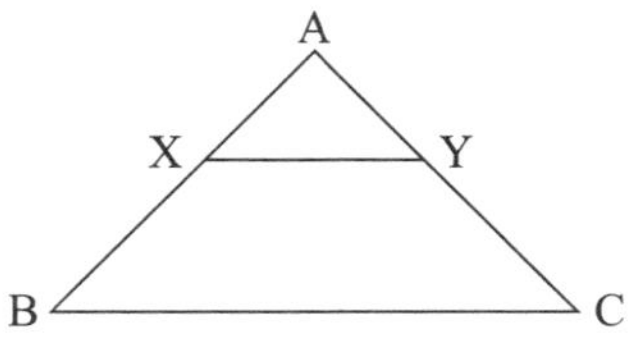

Work out the size of angle BAC.

PS 6 Work out the size of angle r in terms of p and q.

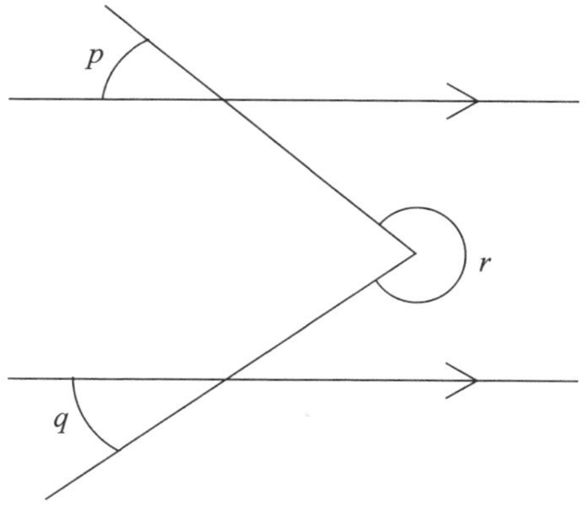

HINTS AND TIPS

Draw a third parallel line that passes through angle *r*.

AU 7 In the diagram, AB is parallel to CD.

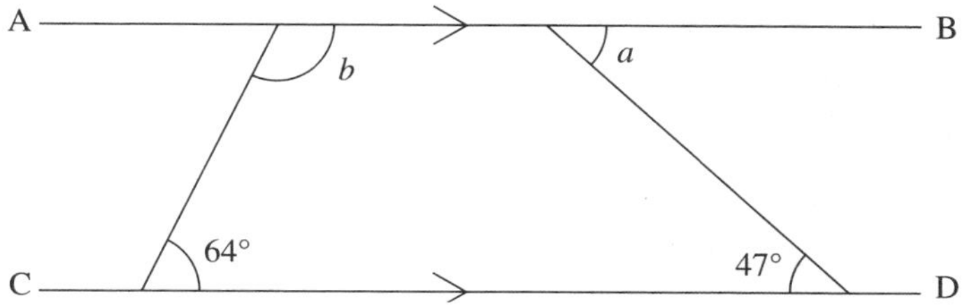

Explain why $a + b = 163$ degrees.

10.7 Special quadrilaterals

HOMEWORK 10G

1 For each of these trapeziums, calculate the sizes of the lettered angles.

a

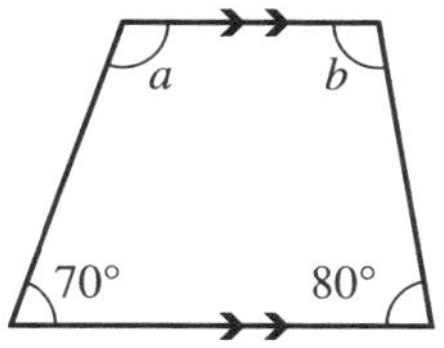

b

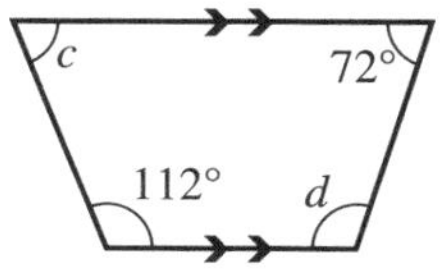

c

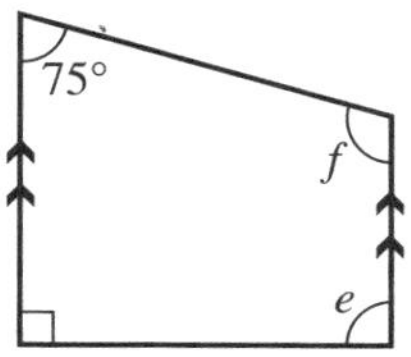

2 For each of these parallelograms, calculate the sizes of the lettered angles.

a

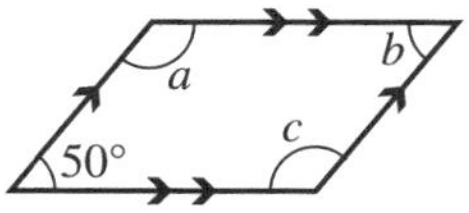

b

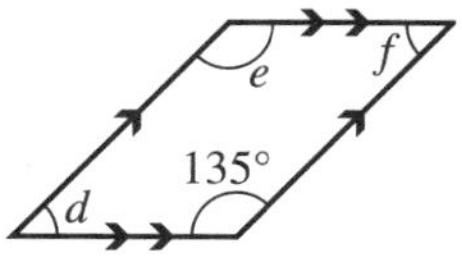

c

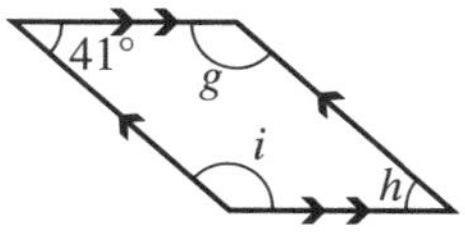

3 For each of these kites, calculate the sizes of the lettered angles.

a

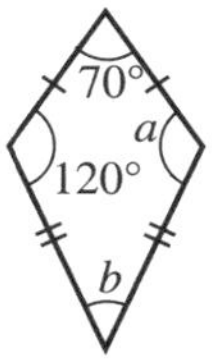

b

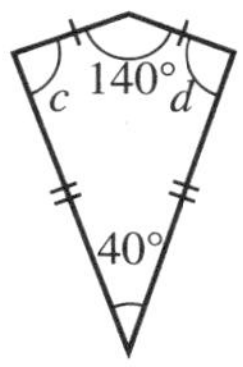

c

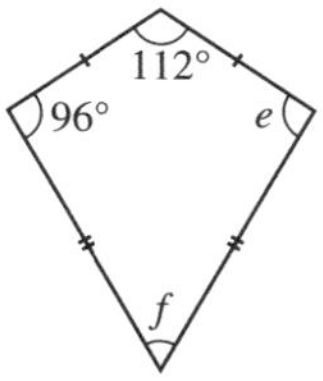

D

4 For each of these rhombuses, calculate the sizes of the lettered angles.

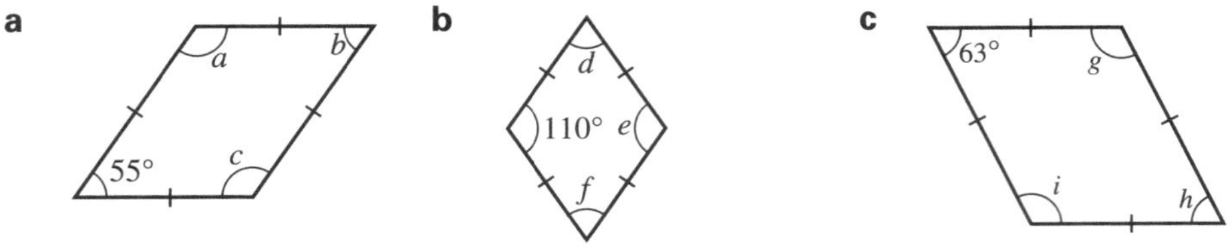

FM 5 The diagram shows the side wall of a barn. The owner wants the angle between the roof and the horizontal to be no less than 20 degrees, so that rain will run off quickly. What can you say about the size of angles A and D?

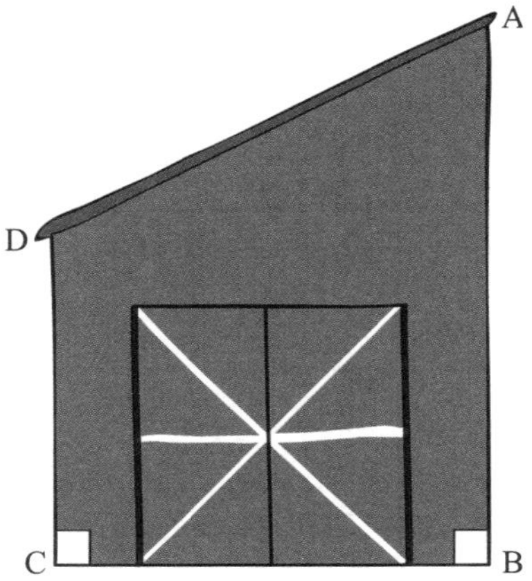

PS 6 The diagram shows a parallelogram ABCD.
AC is a diagonal.

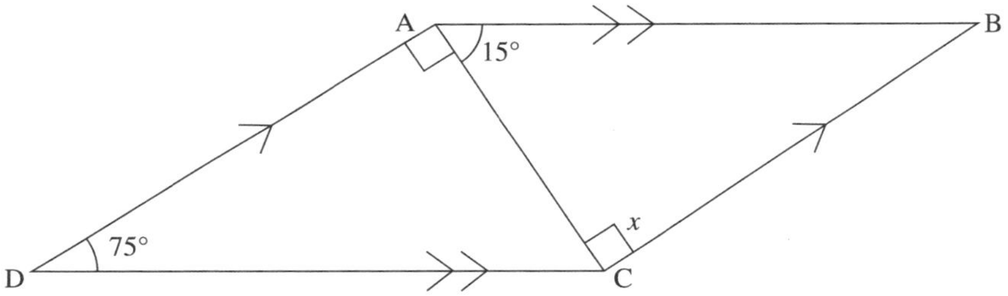

a Find angle x.
b Work out angle BCD.

AU 7 Give two reasons to explain why the trapezium is different from the parallelogram.

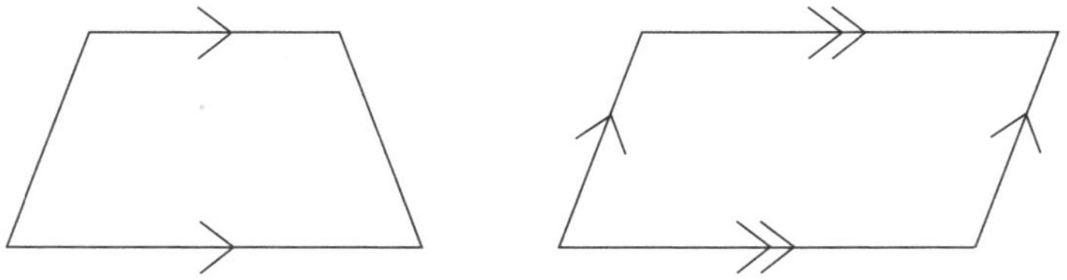

10.8 Bearings

HOMEWORK 10H

D

1 **a** Write down the bearing of B from A.

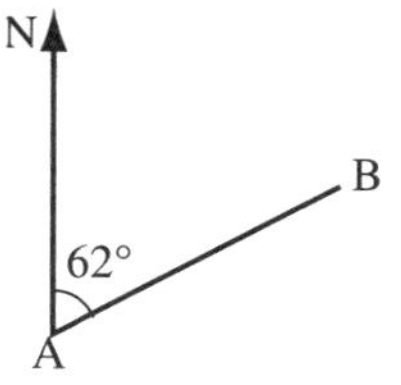

b Write down the bearing of D from C.

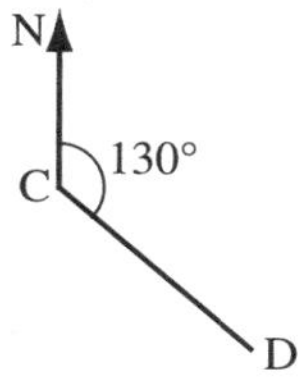

c Write down the bearing of F from E.

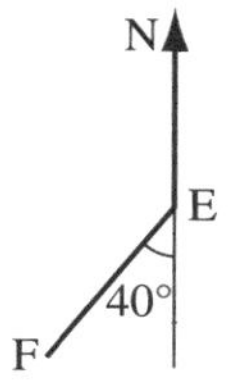

d Write down the bearing of H from G.

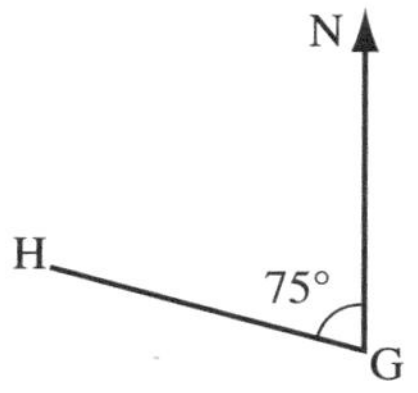

2 On the right is a map of Britain.
By measuring angles, find the bearings of:

a London from Edinburgh
b London from Cardiff
c Edinburgh from Cardiff
d Cardiff from London.

FM 3 An aircraft flies directly from London to Paris.
The diagram shows the aircraft's flight path.

a Write down the three-figure bearing of Paris from London.
b Work out the actual distance from London to Paris.
c The aircraft flies directly back to London.
What is the three-figure bearing of London from Paris?

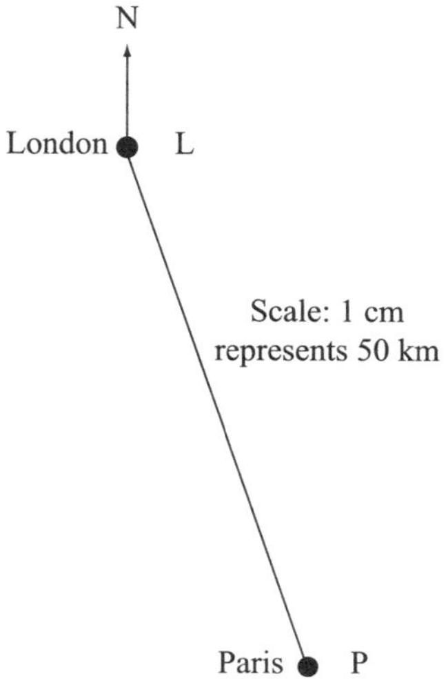

D

PS 4 **a** The bearing of B from A is $x°$.
What is the bearing of A from B?

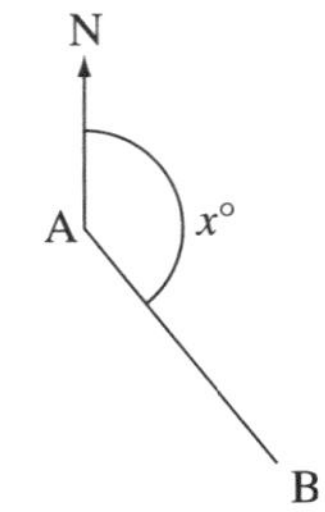

b The bearing of Y from X is $y°$.
What is the bearing of X from Y?

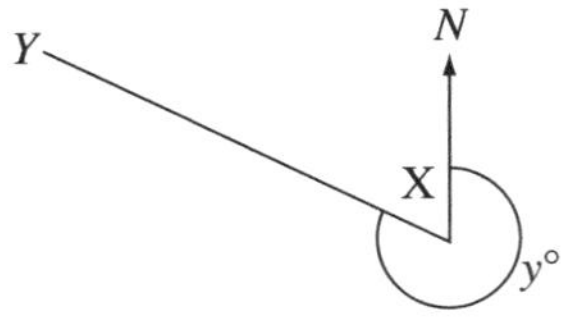

5 Town B is 40 km from Town A and on a bearing of 050°.
Town C is 60 km from Town A and on a bearing of 300°.
Make a scale drawing to find the bearing of Town B from Town C.

FM 6 A ship is sailing at a bearing of 324° when it receives an order to change course to due East. Through how many degrees should it turn?

PS 7 The three towns, A, B and C, form an equilateral triangle. B is due north of A. The bearing of C from A is 060°. What is the bearing of C from B?

Functional Maths Activity

Back bearings

The three-figure bearing of B from A is 060°.

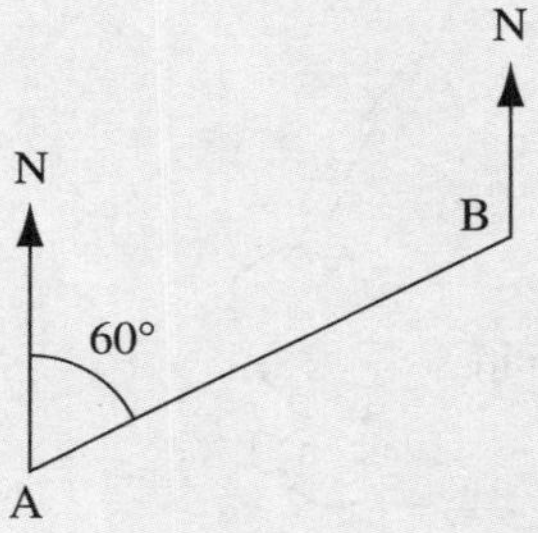

The three-figure bearing of A from B is known as a *back bearing*.

The diagram below shows that the back bearing of A from B is 240°

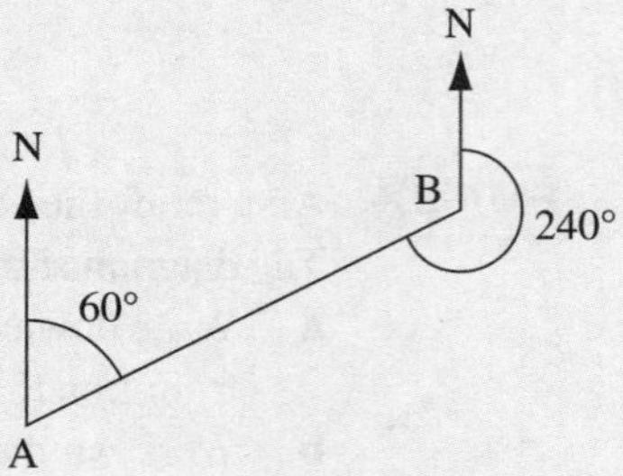

Functional Maths Activity (continued)

Trevor is taking an examination for his pilot's licence.
Here is one of his questions.

The map shows three airports in England.

a Use the map to find the three-figure bearing for each of the following flights:

i Newcastle from Manchester

ii Heathrow from Newcastle

iii Manchester from Heathrow.

b Calculate the back bearing for each flight.

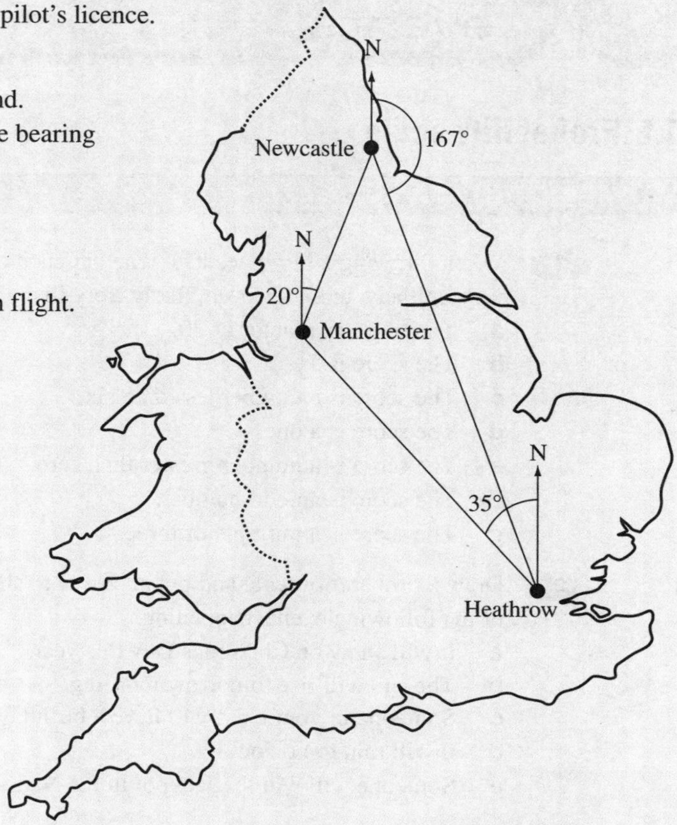

11 Probability: Probability of events

11.1 Probability scale

HOMEWORK 11A

G

1 When throwing a fair dice, state whether each of the following events are impossible, very unlikely, unlikely, even, likely, very likely or certain.

a The score is a factor of 20.
b The score is $3\frac{1}{2}$.
c The score is a number less than six.
d The score is a one.
e The score is a number greater than zero.
f The score is an odd number.
g The score is a multiple of three.

2 Draw a probability scale and put an arrow to show approximately the probability of each of the following events happening.

a It will snow on Christmas Day this year.
b The sun will rise tomorrow morning.
c Someone in your class will have a birthday this month.
d It will rain tomorrow.
e Someone will win the Jackpot in the National Lottery this week.

3 Give an event of your own where you think the probability is:

a impossible **b** very unlikely **c** unlikely **d** evens
e likely **f** very likely **g** certain.

PS 4 'What is the probability of rolling dice and getting a total of more than 3?' asked Mr Ball. 'Choose from impossible, unlikely, even, likely, certain.'
Elliott said, 'It must depend on how many dice I use sir.'
Is Elliott correct? Explain your answer.

AU 5 'I have bought 10 raffle tickets this week, so I have a very good chance of winning.'
Explain what might be wrong with this statement.

11.2 Calculating probabilities

HOMEWORK 11B

Example A bag contains five red balls and three blue balls. A ball is taken out at random.
What is the probability that it is: **a** red **b** blue **c** green?

a There are five red balls out of a total of eight, so P(red) = $\frac{5}{8}$.
b There are three blue balls out of a total of eight, so P(blue) = $\frac{3}{8}$.
c There are no green balls, so P(green) = 0.

F

E

1 When drawing a card from a well-shuffled pack of cards, what is the probability of each of the following events? Remember to cancel down the probability fraction if possible.

a Drawing an Ace.
b Drawing a picture card.
c Drawing a Diamond.
d Drawing a Queen or a King.
e Drawing the Ace of Spades.
f Drawing a red Jack.
g Drawing a Club or a Heart.

2 The numbers 1 to 10 inclusive are placed in a hat. Irene takes a number out of the hat without looking. What is the probability that she draws:

a the number 10
b an odd number
c a number greater than 4
d a prime number
e a number between 5 and 9?

3 A bag contains two blue balls, three red balls and four green balls. Frank takes a ball from the bag without looking. What is the probability that he takes out:

a a blue ball **b** a red ball **c** a ball that is not green **d** a yellow ball?

4 In a prize raffle there are 50 tickets: 10 coloured red, 10 coloured blue and the rest coloured white. What is the probability that the first ticket drawn out is:

a red **b** blue **c** white **d** red or white **e** not blue?

5 A bag contains 15 coloured balls. Three are red, five are blue and the rest are black. Paul takes a ball at random from the bag.

a Find:
  i P(he chooses a red) **ii** P(he chooses a blue) **iii** P(he chooses a black).
b Add together the three probabilities. What do you notice?
c Explain your answer to part **b**.

6 Boris knows that when he plays a game of chess, he has a 65% chance of winning a game and a 15% chance of losing a game. What is the probability that he draws a game?

FM 7 Adam, Emily, Katie, Daniel and Maria are all sitting in Mrs Odell's class during lunch break. Mrs Odell wants two of these students to tidy a cupboard.

a Write down all the possible combinations of two students.
b How many pairs give two girls?
c What is the probability of choosing two girls at random?
d How many pairs give a girl and a boy?
e What is the probability of, at random, choosing a boy and a girl?
f What is the probability of choosing two boys?

PS 8 The following information is known about the following classes at a school.

Year	Y7		Y8		Y9		Y10		Y11	
Class	Boys	Girls	Boys	Girls	Boys	Girls	Boys	Girls	Boys	Girls
Pets	7	8	8	9	10	9	8	9	8	11
No pets	4	5	4	5	6	8	5	6	5	4

A class representative is chosen at random from each class.
Which class has the best chance of choosing a boy who also has a pet as its representative?

AU 9 George is playing a game of tennis.
His sister says, 'He either wins or loses, so he must have an even chance of winning.'
Explain why George's sister might not be correct.

11.3 Probability that an outcome of an event will not happen

HOMEWORK 11C

Example What is the probability of not picking an Ace from a pack of cards?

First, find the probability of picking an Ace: P (picking an Ace) = $\frac{4}{52} = \frac{1}{13}$
Therefore, P (not picking an Ace) = $1 - \frac{1}{13} = \frac{12}{13}$

1 **a** The probability of winning a prize in a tombola is $\frac{1}{25}$. What is the probability of not winning a prize in the tombola?
b The probability that it will rain tomorrow is 65%. What is the probability that it will not rain tomorrow?
c The probability that Josie wins a game of tennis is 0.8. What is the probability that she loses a game?
d The probability of getting a double six when throwing two dice is $\frac{1}{36}$. What is the probability of not getting a double six?

2 Harvinder picks a card from a pack of well-shuffled playing cards. Find the probability that she picks:
a **i** a King **ii** a card that is not a King
b **i** a Spade **ii** a card that is not a Spade
c **i** a 9 or a 10 **ii** neither a 9 nor a 10.

3 The following letters are put into a bag.

A B R A C A D A B R A

a Stan takes a letter at random. What is the probability that:
i he takes a letter A **ii** he does not take a letter A?
b Pat takes an R and keeps it. Stan now takes a letter from the remaining letters.
i What is the probability that he takes a letter A?
ii What is the probability that he does not take a letter A?

FM 4 The starting row in a board game is:

Start	Chelsea Park	Take a Chance 	London Road	Carter Road	Pay £500 in tax	Banner Road	Struen Road	Rest area

You roll a dice and move, from the start, the number of places shown by the dice.
What is the probability of **not** landing on:
a A purple square?
b The Pay Tax square?
c A coloured square?

PS 5 Elijah and Harris are playing a board game. Each player rolls one dice to move.
On the next go, Elijah will have to miss a turn if he rolls an odd number. Harris will miss a turn if he rolls a 1 or a 2.
Who has the best chance of not missing a turn on their next go?

AU 6 Arran is told, 'The chance of you losing this game is only 0.1'
Arran says, 'So my chance of winning is 0.9'
Explain why Arran might be wrong.

Functional Maths Activity

School fete

The following grid was used in a school fete as a 'roll a 10p' game.
A 10p coin was rolled down a chute to roll onto the board, which measured 21 cm by 21 cm.

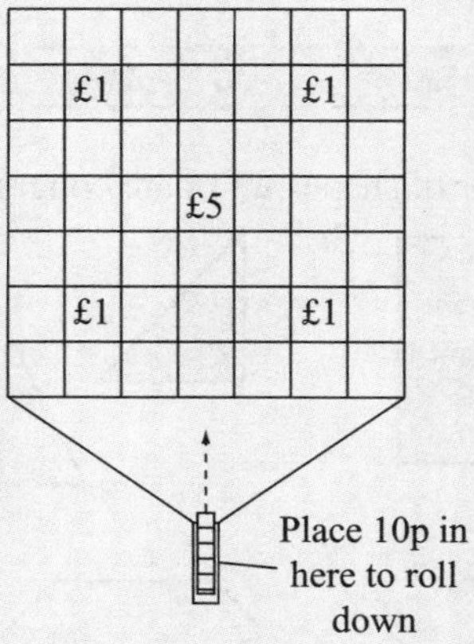

If the 10p landed:

- completely on any square, the player got their 10p back
- completely on a square marked £1, the player won £1
- completely on the square marked £5, the player won £5

1 Conduct an experiment to find out what the probability is of each of these outcomes: a player winning £5, a player winning £1, or a player winning their money back.

2 Use your answers to Question **1** to estimate how much money this game would win or lose if 500 people were to play it.

12 Geometry: Transformations 1

12.1 Congruent shapes

HOMEWORK 12A

1 State whether each pair of shapes **a** to **f** are congruent or not.

a

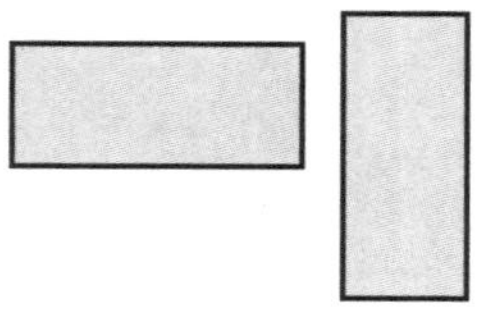

b

c

d

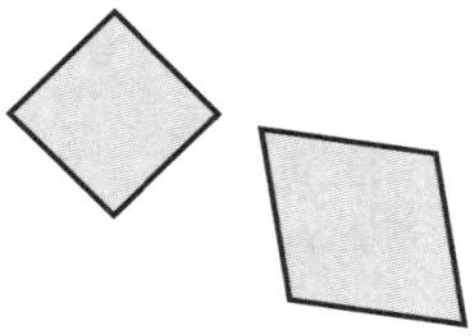

e

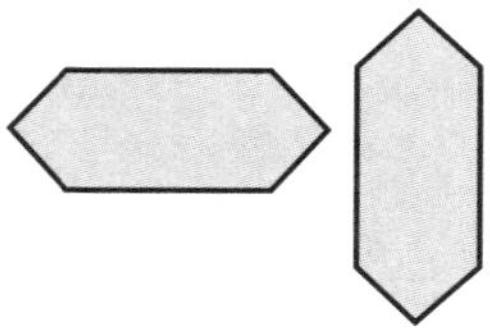

f

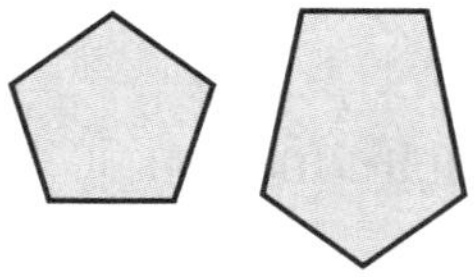

2 Which figure in each group of shapes is not congruent to the other two?

a

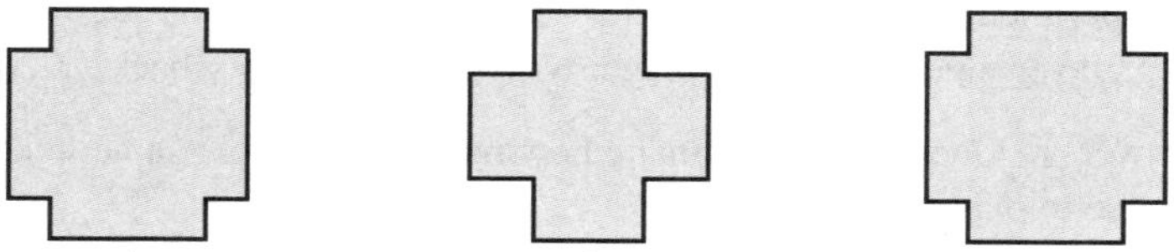

1 2 3

b

1 2 3

c

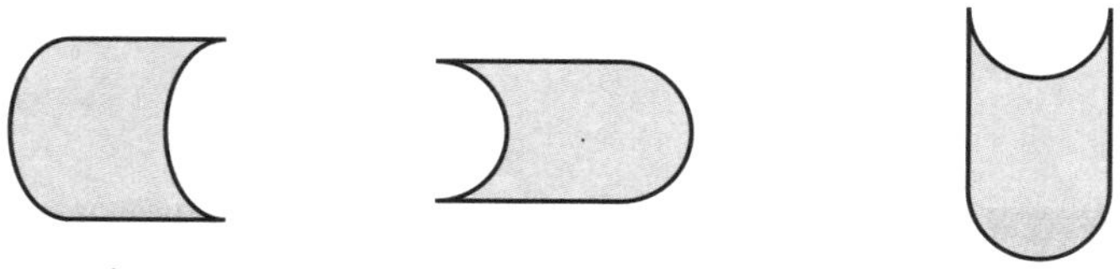

1 2 3

d

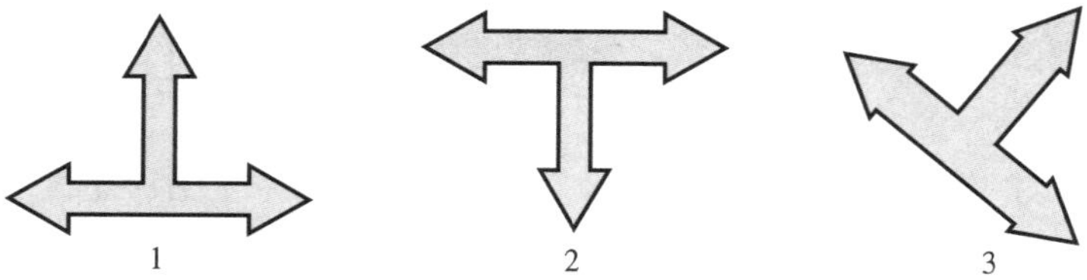

1 2 3

FM **3** While she was sitting in a doctors waiting room, Katrina looked at a simple design made of wood built into the wall as shown.

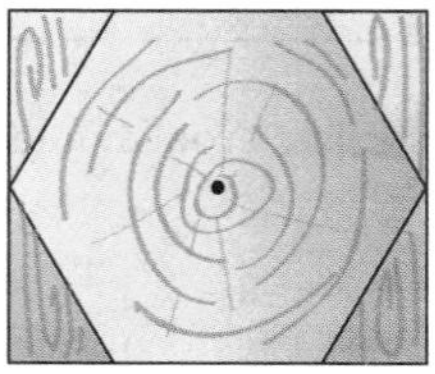

a What is the name of this six-sided regular shape?

b If you were to label the vertices ABCDEF and the centre O, how many other shapes inside the shape are congruent to:

i triangle ABC?
ii quadrilateral ABCD?
iii triangle ACE?
iv rectangle ABDE?
v triangle AOB?
vi triangle ABD?
vii pentagon ABCDE?

4 The kite ABCD is shown on the right. The diagonals AC and BD intersect at X.

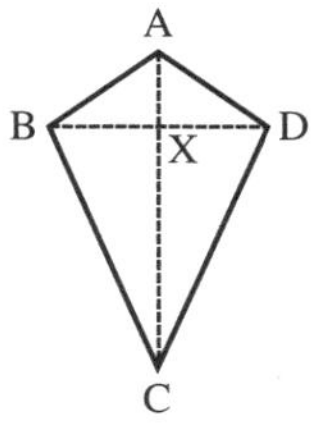

Which of the following statements are true?

a Triangle ABC is congruent to triangle ACD.
b Triangle ABD is congruent to triangle BCD.
c Triangle XBC is congruent to triangle XCD.

PS **5** There are two single-digit numbers that could be considered congruent.
How many numbers less than one hundred can you write down that could be considered congruent with another?
Write all these numbers down in their congruent pairs.

AU **6** Uzma and Pete are looking at a stained glass window. Uzma says to Pete, 'It's amazing how they can create such a window with different-sized congruent shapes.'
Pete replies, 'Yes, you are right.'
How can this statement be correct?

12.2 Tessellations

HOMEWORK 12B

D

1 On squared paper, show how each of these shapes tessellate. You should draw at least six shapes.

a

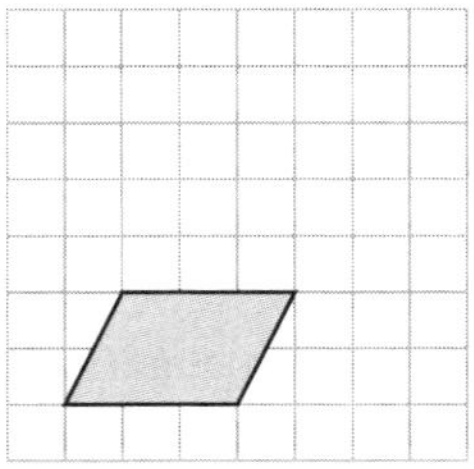

b

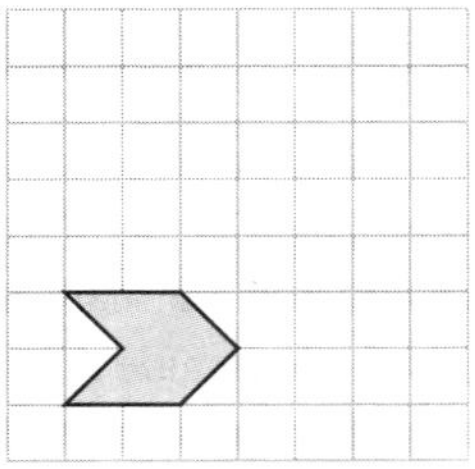

c

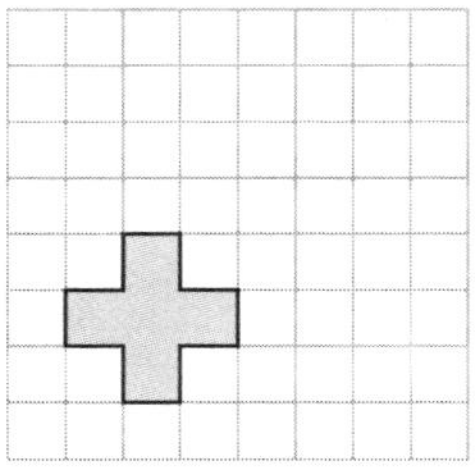

d

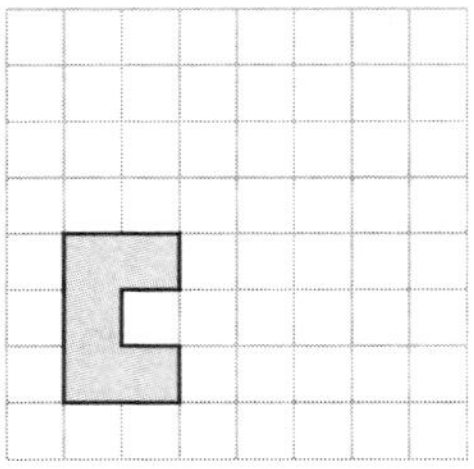

2 Use isometric paper to show how a regular hexagon tessellates.

PS 3 Jeff says, 'All hexagons tessellate.'
Investigate this statement to see if you think it may be true.

AU 4 Explain what is meant by a shape tessellating.

Problem-solving Activity

Transformation problem

Look at the diagram showing shape A and shape B.

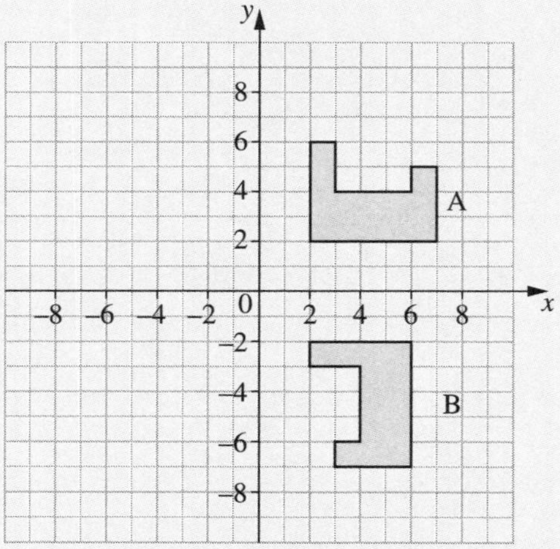

Describe, using three combined transformations, how shape A can be transformed into shape B.

13 Geometry and measures: Constructions

13.1 Constructing triangles

HOMEWORK 13A

1 Accurately draw each of the following triangles.

a

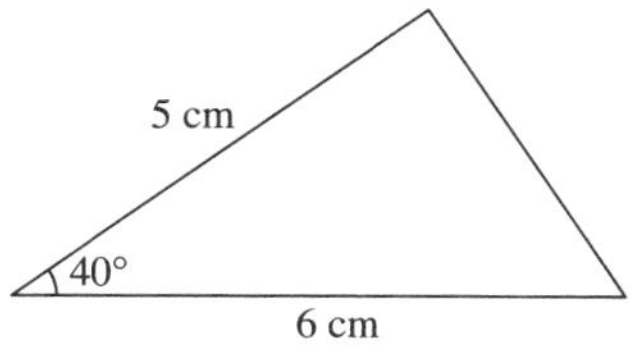

b

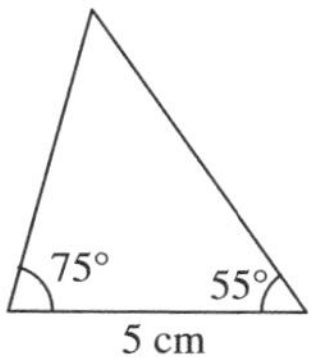

c

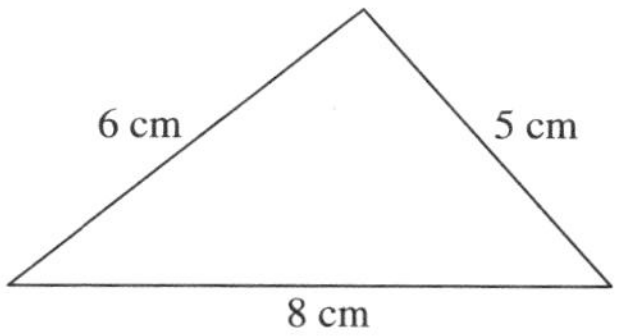

d

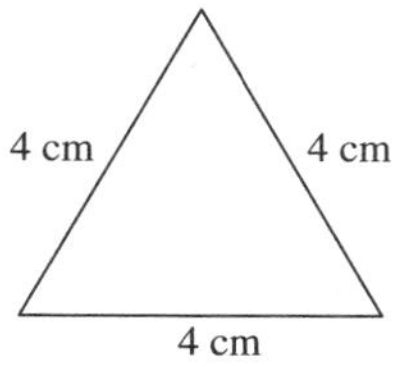

e

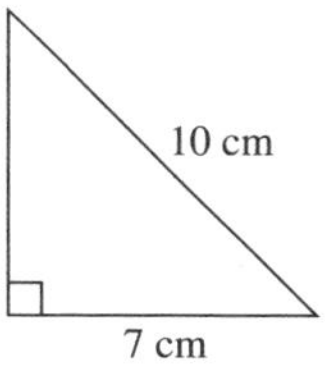

2 Draw a triangle ABC with AB = 6 cm, ∠A = 60° and ∠B = 50°.

3

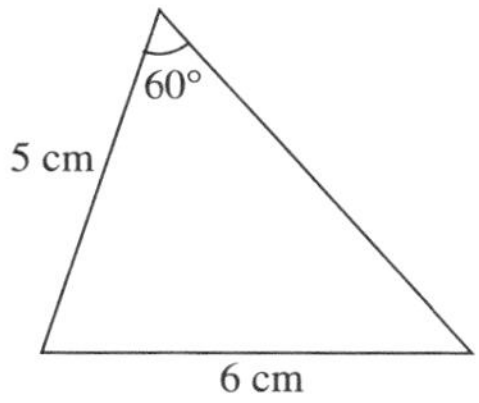

Explain why you can or cannot draw this triangle accurately.

4 **a** Accurately draw the shape on the right.
b What is the name of the shape you have drawn?

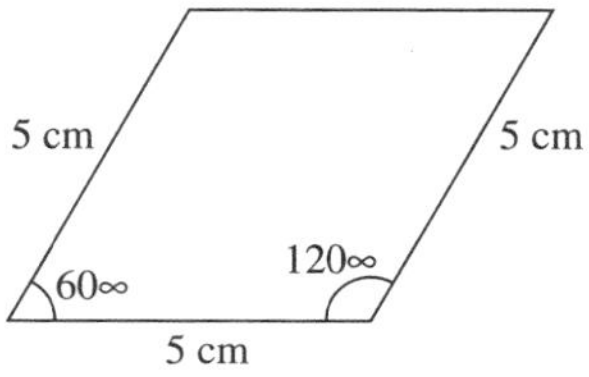

AU 5 Shehab says ‘As long as I know two sides of a triangle and one angle I can draw it.’
Is Shehab correct? If not, explain why.

PS 6 You are asked to construct a triangle with two sides of 9 cm and 10 cm and an angle of 60°.
Sketch all the possible triangles you could construct from this description.

D

14 Number: Further number skills

14.1 Long multiplication

HOMEWORK 14A

F

1 24×13 **2** 33×17 **3** 54×42 **4** 89×23 **5** 58×53

6 176×14 **7** 235×16 **8** 439×21 **9** 572×35 **10** 678×57

FM **11** Andy needs enough tiles to cover 12 m^2 in his bathroom. It takes 25 tiles to cover 1 m^2. It is recommended to buy 20% more to allow for cutting.
Tiles are sold in boxes of 16. Andy buys 24 packs. Does he have enough tiles?

FM **12** A TV rental shop buys TVs for £110 each.
The shop need to make at least 10% on each TV to cover overheads.
On average each TV is rented for 40 weeks at £3.50 per week.
Does the shop cover its overheads?

FM **13** Mrs Woodhead saves £14 per week towards her fuel bills.
Her annual fuel bills are £900.
Does she save enough?

FM **14** Sylvia has a part-time job and is paid £18 for every day she works. Last year she worked for 148 days. She saves all her income towards a summer holiday that costs £2000. She changes the extra into Euros at an exchange rate of £1 = €1.20. How many Euros does she get?

PS **15** A concert hall has 48 rows of seats with 32 seats in a row. What is the maximum capacity of the hall?

PS AU **16** A room measuring 6 metres by 8 metres is to be carpeted. The carpet costs £19 per square metre.

a Estimate the cost of the carpet.

b Calculate the exact cost of the carpet.

14.2 Long division

HOMEWORK 14B

F

1 $312 \div 13$ **2** $480 \div 15$ **3** $697 \div 17$ **4** $792 \div 22$ **5** $806 \div 26$

6 $532 \div 28$ **7** $736 \div 32$ **8** $595 \div 35$ **9** $948 \div 41$ **10** $950 \div 53$

FM **11** The organiser of a church fete needs 1000 balloons. She has a budget of £30. Each packet contains 25 balloons and costs 85p. Does she have enough?

FM **12** The annual subscription fee to join a Fishing Club is £42. The treasurer of the club has collected £1134 in fees. The annual rental for the fishing pond is £2000. How many more members need to join so that they can pay the rental?

FM **13** A coach firm charges £504 for 36 people to go Christmas shopping on a day trip to Calais. Mary takes £150. The cost of the coach is shared equally between the passengers. Mary wants to buy a game costing €50 for each of her 4 grandchildren. The exchange rate is £1 = €1.25. Does she have enough?

PS AU **14** Allan is a market gardener and has 420 bulbs to plant. He plants them out in rows with 18 bulbs to a row. How many complete rows will there be?

14.3 Arithmetic with decimal numbers

HOMEWORK 14C

Example 1 5.852 will round off to 5.85 to two decimal places

Example 2 7.156 will round off to 7.16 to two decimal places

Example 3 0.284 will round off to 0.3 to one decimal place

Example 4 15.3518 will round off to 15.4 to one decimal place

1 Round each of the following numbers to one decimal place.

a 3.73 **b** 8.69 **c** 5.34 **d** 18.75 **e** 0.423
f 26.288 **g** 3.755 **h** 10.056 **i** 11.08 **j** 12.041

2 Round each of the following numbers to two decimal places.

a 6.721 **b** 4.457 **c** 1.972 **d** 3.485 **e** 5.807
f 2.564 **g** 21.799 **h** 12.985 **i** 2.302 **j** 5.555

3 Round each of the following to the number of decimal places indicated.

a 4.572 (1 dp) **b** 0.085 (2 dp) **c** 5.7159 (3 dp) **d** 4.558 (2 dp)
e 2.099 (2 dp) **f** 0.7629 (3 dp) **g** 7.124 (1 dp) **h** 8.903 (2 dp)
i 23.7809 (3 dp) **j** 0.99 (1 dp)

4 Round each of the following to the nearest whole number.

a 6.7 **b** 9.3 **c** 2.8 **d** 7.5 **e** 8.38
f 2.82 **g** 2.18 **h** 1.55 **i** 5.252 **j** 3.999

FM **5** Trevor buys the following car accessories:
Shampoo £4.99; Wax £7.29; Wheel cleaner £4.81; Dusters £1.08.
By rounding each price to the nearest pound, work out an estimate of the total cost of the items.

AU **6** Which of the following are correct roundings of the number 9.281?

9 9.2 9.28 9.3 9.30

PS **7** When a number is rounded to two decimal places, the answer is 6.14.
Which of these could be the number?

6.140 6.143 6.148 6.15

HOMEWORK 14D

Example Work out 4.2 + 8 + 12.93. Set out the sum as follows:

Remember to keep the points in the same column.

$$\begin{array}{r} 4.20 \\ 8.00 \\ +\ \underline{12.93} \\ \underline{25.13} \\ {\scriptstyle 1\,1} \end{array}$$

1 Work out each of these.

a	7.3 + 2.6	**b**	15.7 + 5.6	**c**	33.5 + 6.8	**d**	8.5 + 4.82
e	3.26 + 4.5	**f**	2.75 + 9.84	**g**	24.5 + 6.3	**h**	8.4 + 12.8
i	13.75 + 8.5	**j**	7.08 + 0.7	**k**	7 + 2.96 + 3.1	**l**	8.5 + 7.36 + 12.1

2 Work out each of these.

a	5.8 – 3.4	**b**	7.3 – 2.8	**c**	4.6 – 2.7	**d**	9.7 – 4.7
e	8.35 – 4.24	**f**	9.74 – 3.81	**g**	9.04 – 5.72	**h**	3.62 – 1.85
i	6 – 3.3	**j**	8 – 7.4	**k**	12 – 3.2	**l**	7.2 – 4.72

AU 3 Olivia has £3.80 left after buying a toy for £8.99.

a How much did she have before she bought the toy?

b She then goes home by tram.

After paying her tram fare she has £1.05 left.

How much is the tram fare?

FM 4 A piece of cloth is 2.7 metres long.

Is it possible to get two pieces of lengths 1.8 metres and 0.8 metres from the cloth?

PS 5 Copy and complete the following.

a 16.3 + ... = 20.7

b 41.5 + ... = 67.9

c ...... + 3.4 = 9.2

d ...... + 7.35 = 8.26

6 Copy and complete the following.

a 21.3 – ...... = 13.8

b 70.5 – ...... = 48.2

c ...... – 6.3 = 8.4

d ...... – 12.5 = 8.7

HOMEWORK 14E

Example 1 4.5 × 3 =
$$\begin{array}{r} 4.5 \\ \underline{\times\quad 3} \\ \underline{13.5} \\ {\scriptstyle 1} \end{array}$$

Example 2 8.25 ÷ 5 =
$$\begin{array}{r} 1.\ 6\ 5 \\ 5\,\overline{)\,8.{}^{3}2{}^{2}5} \end{array}$$

Example 3 5.7 ÷ 2 =
$$\begin{array}{r} 2.\ 8\ 5 \\ 2\,\overline{)\,5.{}^{1}7{}^{1}0} \end{array}$$

1 Evaluate each of these.

a 2.3 × 3 **b** 4.8 × 2 **c** 4.6 × 4 **d** 15.3 × 5 **e** 26.4 × 8

F

2 Evaluate each of these.
a 2.14 × 2 **b** 3.45 × 3 **c** 5.47 × 6 **d** 4.44 × 8 **e** 0.25 × 9

3 Evaluate each of these.
a 4.8 ÷ 2 **b** 7.6 ÷ 4 **c** 7.2 ÷ 3 **d** 7.35 ÷ 5 **e** 0.78 ÷ 6

4 Evaluate each of these.
a 4.5 ÷ 2 **b** 7.2 ÷ 5 **c** 3.4 ÷ 4 **d** 13.1 ÷ 5 **e** 6.3 ÷ 8

E

FM 5 Crisps are sold in packs of six for £1.32 or packs of eight for £1.92. Which are better value?

FM 6 Steve takes his wife and three children on a day trip by train to London.
a The tickets cost £26.60 for each adult and £12.85 for each child. How much do the tickets cost Steve altogether?
b While they are in London, they decide to go on a bus tour.
Tickets are £22 for adults and £10 for children.
Steve only has enough money if he can negotiate £2 off the price of each ticket.
How much money does he have?

HOMEWORK 14F

Example Evaluate 4.27 × 34 =

```
   4.27
×    34
  17.08  (multiply by 4)
 128.10  (multiply by 3 and keep points in same column)
 145.18
```

E

1 Evaluate each of these.
a 3.12 × 14 **b** 5.24 × 15 **c** 1.36 × 22 **d** 7.53 × 25 **e** 27.1 × 32

2 Find the total cost of each of the following purchases.
a 24 litres of petrol at £1.22 per litre
b 18 pints of milk at £0.56 per pint.
c 14 magazines at £2.75 per copy.

FM 3 The table shows the exchange rate for various currencies

Currency	Exchange rate
Euro (€)	£1 = €1.15
American dollar ($)	£1 = $1.55
Swiss franc (F)	£1 = 1.65F

a Douglas changes £25 into Euros. How many Euros does he get?
b Martin changes £32 into dollars. How many dollars does he get?
c Pauline changes £45 into francs. How many francs does she get?

PS 4 Jordan says that he can change multiplications into easier multiplications by changing the multiplication around as shown:
To work out 0.8 × 72, he does 7.2 × 8
Use his method to work out 0.6 × 21

AU 5 Pola is paid £9.71 per hour for working 30 hours each week.
She saves half of her pay.
How many weeks will it take her to save £1000?

HOMEWORK 14G

To multiply one decimal number by another decimal number:

- First, do the whole calculation as if the decimal points were not there.
- Then, count the total number of decimal places in the two decimal numbers. This gives the number of decimal places in the answer.

Example Evaluate 3.42×0.2

Ignoring the decimal points gives the following calculation: $342 \times 2 = 684$

Now, 3.42 has two decimal places and 0.2 has one decimal place. So, the total number of decimal places in the answer is three, which gives $3.42 \times 0.2 = 0.684$

E

1 Evaluate each of these.

a 2.3×0.2 **b** 5.2×0.3 **c** 4.6×0.4 **d** 0.2×0.3 **e** 0.4×0.7
f 0.5×0.5 **g** 12.6×0.6 **h** 7.2×0.7 **i** 1.4×1.2 **j** 2.6×1.5

FM **2** Kerry wants to buy a plank of wood 6.5 metres long. It costs £1.25 per metre. She has £10. Can she afford it?

D

3 For each of the following:

i estimate the answer by first rounding off each number to the nearest whole number.
ii calculate the exact answer, and then, by doing a subtraction, calculate how much out your answer to part **i** is.

a 3.7×2.4 **b** 4.8×3.1 **c** 5.1×4.2 **d** 6.5×2.5

PS AU **4** **a** Use any method to work out 15×16

b Use your answer to work out:
i 1.5×1.6
ii 0.75×3.2
iii 4.5×1.6

14.4 Arithmetic with fractions

HOMEWORK 14H

Example 1 Express 0.32 as a fraction.

$0.32 = \frac{32}{100}$. This cancels down to $\frac{8}{25}$.

Example 2 Express $\frac{3}{8}$ as a decimal. $\frac{3}{8} = 3 \div 8 = 0.375$.

$$\begin{array}{r} 0.\,3\,7\,5 \\ 8\,\overline{)3.{}^{3}0{}^{6}0{}^{4}0} \end{array}$$

Notice how the extra zeros have been added.

E

1 Change each of these decimals to fractions, cancelling down where possible.

a 0.3 **b** 0.8 **c** 0.9 **d** 0.07 **e** 0.08
f 0.15 **g** 0.75 **h** 0.48 **i** 0. 32 **j** 0.27

2 Change each of these fractions to decimals.

a $\frac{1}{4}$ **b** $\frac{2}{5}$ **c** $\frac{7}{10}$ **d** $\frac{9}{20}$ **e** $\frac{7}{8}$

3 Put each of the following sets of numbers in order with the smallest first. It is easier to change the fractions into decimals first.

a $0.3, 0.2, \frac{2}{5}$ **b** $\frac{7}{10}, 0.8, 0.6$ **c** $0.4, \frac{1}{4}, 0.2$

d $\frac{3}{10}, 0.32, 0.29$ **e** $0.81, \frac{4}{5}, 0.78$

FM 4 Two shops are advertising the same skirts.

Which shop has the better offer?
Give a reason for your answer.

PS 5 Which is bigger: $\frac{5}{6}$ or 0.8?
Show your working.

PS 6 Which is smaller: $\frac{1}{3}$ or 0.3?
Show your working.

PS 7 Complete this statement with a fraction.
$\frac{1}{3}$ of 45 is the same as ...... of 30.

HOMEWORK 14I

1 Evaluate the following.

a $\frac{1}{2}+\frac{1}{5}$ **b** $\frac{1}{2}+\frac{1}{3}$ **c** $\frac{1}{3}+\frac{1}{10}$ **d** $\frac{3}{8}+\frac{1}{3}$

e $\frac{3}{4}+\frac{1}{5}$ **f** $\frac{1}{3}+\frac{2}{5}$ **g** $\frac{3}{5}+\frac{3}{8}$ **h** $\frac{1}{2}+\frac{2}{5}$

2 Evaluate the following.

a $\frac{1}{2}+\frac{1}{4}$ **b** $\frac{1}{3}+\frac{1}{6}$ **c** $\frac{3}{5}+\frac{1}{10}$ **d** $\frac{5}{8}+\frac{1}{4}$

3 Evaluate the following.

a $\frac{7}{8}-\frac{3}{4}$ **b** $\frac{4}{5}-\frac{1}{2}$ **c** $\frac{2}{3}-\frac{1}{5}$ **d** $\frac{3}{4}-\frac{2}{5}$

4 Evaluate the following.

a $\frac{5}{8}+\frac{3}{4}$ **b** $\frac{1}{2}+\frac{3}{5}$ **c** $\frac{5}{6}+\frac{1}{4}$ **d** $\frac{2}{3}+\frac{3}{4}$

5 Evaluate the following.

a $2\frac{1}{3}+1\frac{1}{4}$ **b** $3\frac{7}{10}+2\frac{3}{4}$ **c** $5\frac{3}{8}-2\frac{1}{3}$ **d** $4\frac{2}{5}-2\frac{5}{6}$

6 At a football club half of the players are English, a quarter are Scottish and one-sixth are Italian. The rest are Irish. What fraction of players at the club are Irish?

7 On a firm's coach trip, half the people were employees, two-fifths were partners of the employees. The rest were children. What fraction of the people were children?

AU 8 Five-eighths of the 35 000 crowd were male. How many females were in the crowd?

C

9 What is four-fifths of sixty-five added to five-sixths of fifty-four?

10 Find two fractions with a sum of $\frac{11}{12}$.

HOMEWORK 14J

E

1 Evaluate the following, leaving your answer in its simplest form.

a $\frac{1}{2} \times \frac{2}{3}$ **b** $\frac{3}{4} \times \frac{2}{5}$ **c** $\frac{3}{5} \times \frac{1}{2}$ **d** $\frac{3}{7} \times \frac{2}{3}$ **e** $\frac{2}{3} \times \frac{5}{6}$

f $\frac{1}{3} \times \frac{3}{5}$ **g** $\frac{2}{3} \times \frac{7}{10}$ **h** $\frac{3}{8} \times \frac{2}{5}$ **i** $\frac{4}{9} \times \frac{3}{8}$ **j** $\frac{4}{5} \times \frac{7}{16}$

D

2 Kris walked three-quarters of the way along Carterknowle Road, which is 3 km long. How far did Kris walk?

AU **3** Jean ate one-fifth of a cake, Les ate a half of what was left. Nick ate the rest. What fraction of the cake did Nick eat?

FM **4** **a** Billie made a cast that weighed five and three quarter kilograms. Four-fifths of this weight is water. What is the weight of the water in Billie's cast?

b 1 litre of water weighs 1 kg. A jug holds 2 litres of water. How many times does Billie need to fill the jug to have enough water to make the cast.

C

5 Evaluate the following, leaving your answer as a mixed number where possible.

a $1\frac{1}{3} \times 2\frac{1}{4}$ **b** $1\frac{3}{4} \times 1\frac{1}{3}$ **c** $2\frac{1}{2} \times \frac{4}{5}$ **d** $1\frac{2}{3} \times 1\frac{3}{10}$

e $3\frac{1}{4} \times 1\frac{3}{5}$ **f** $2\frac{2}{3} \times 1\frac{3}{4}$ **g** $3\frac{1}{2} \times 1\frac{1}{6}$ **h** $7\frac{1}{2} \times 1\frac{3}{5}$

AU **6** Which is the smaller, $\frac{3}{4}$ of $5\frac{1}{3}$ or $\frac{2}{3}$ of $4\frac{2}{5}$?

FM PS **7** I estimate that I need 60 litres of lemonade for a party.
I buy 24 bottles, which each contain $2\frac{3}{4}$ litres.
Have I bought enough lemonade for the party?

HOMEWORK 14K

C

1 Evaluate the following, leaving your answer as a mixed number where possible.

a $\frac{1}{5} \div \frac{1}{3}$ **b** $\frac{3}{5} \div \frac{3}{8}$ **c** $\frac{4}{5} \div \frac{2}{3}$ **d** $\frac{4}{7} \div \frac{8}{9}$

e $4 \div 1\frac{1}{2}$ **f** $5 \div 3\frac{2}{3}$ **g** $8 \div 1\frac{3}{4}$ **h** $6 \div 1\frac{1}{4}$

i $5\frac{1}{2} \div 1\frac{1}{3}$ **j** $7\frac{1}{2} \div 2\frac{2}{3}$ **k** $1\frac{1}{2} \div 1\frac{1}{5}$ **l** $3\frac{1}{5} \div 3\frac{3}{4}$

FM **2** A pet shop has thirty-six kilograms of hamster food. Tom, who owns the shop, wants to pack this into bags, each containing three-quarters of a kilogram. How many bags can he make in this way?

AU **3** Bob is putting a fence down the side of his garden, it is to be 20 metres long. The fence comes in sections; each one is one and one-third of a metre long. How many sections will Bob need to put the fence all the way down the one side of his garden?

4 An African Bullfrog can jump a distance of $1\frac{1}{4}$ metres in one hop. How many hops would it take an African Bullfrog to hop a distance of 100 metres?

14.5 Multiplying and dividing with negative numbers

HOMEWORK 14L

E

1 Write down the answers to the following.

a -2×4	**b** -3×6	**c** -5×7	**d** -3×-4	**e** -8×-2
f $-14 \div -2$	**g** $-16 \div -4$	**h** $25 \div -5$	**i** $-16 \div -8$	**j** $-8 \div -4$
k 3×-7	**l** 6×-3	**m** 7×-4	**n** -3×-9	**o** -7×-2
p $28 \div -4$	**q** $12 \div -3$	**r** $-40 \div 8$	**s** $-15 \div -3$	**t** $50 \div -2$
u -3×-8	**v** $42 \div -6$	**w** 7×-9	**x** $-24 \div -4$	**y** -7×8

2 Write down the answers to the following.

a $-2 + 4$	**b** $-3 + 6$	**c** $-5 + 7$	**d** $-3 + -4$	**e** $-8 + -2$
f $-14 - -2$	**g** $-16 - -4$	**h** $25 - -5$	**i** $-16 - -8$	**j** $-8 - -4$
k $3 + -7$	**l** $6 + -3$	**m** $7 + -4$	**n** $-3 + -9$	**o** $-7 + -2$
p $28 - -4$	**q** $12 - -3$	**r** $-40 - 8$	**s** $-15 - -3$	**t** $50 - -2$
u $-3 + -8$	**v** $42 - -6$	**w** $7 + -9$	**x** $-24 - -4$	**y** $-7 + 8$

3 What number do you multiply -5 by to get the following?

a 25 **b** -30 **c** 50 **d** -100 **e** 75

AU 4
a Work out 7×-3.
b The average temperature drops by 3°C every day for a week. How much has the temperature dropped altogether by the end of the week?
c The temperature drops by 5°C for the next two days. Write down the calculation to work the total drop in temperature over these two days.

PS 5 Put these calculations in order from lowest to highest.

$-20 \div 2$ -8×-1 $-24 \div -6$ -7×2

14.6 Approximation of calculations

HOMEWORK 14M

E

1 Round each of the following numbers to one significant figure.

a 46 313	**b** 57 123	**c** 30 569	**d** 94 558	**e** 85 299
f 54.26	**g** 85.18	**h** 27.09	**i** 96.432	**j** 167.77
k 0.5388	**l** 0.2823	**m** 0.005 84	**n** 0.047 85	**o** 0.000 876
p 9.9	**q** 89.5	**r** 90.78	**s** 199	**t** 999.99

AU 2 What is the least and the greatest number of people that can be found in these towns?

Hellaby	population 900 (to one significant figure)
Hook	population 650 (to two significant figures)
Hundleton	population 1050 (to three significant figures)

D

PS 3 A baker estimates that she has baked 100 loaves. She is correct to one significant figure.
She sells two loaves and now has 90 loaves to one significant figure.
How many could she have had to start with?
Work out all possible answers.

AU 4 There are 500 cars in a car park to one significant figure.
What is the least possible number of cars that could enter the car park so that there are 700 cars in the car park to one significant figure?

HOMEWORK 14N

D

1 Find approximate answers to the following sums.

a 4324 × 6.71	**b** 6170 × 7.311	**c** 72.35 × 3.142
d 4709 × 3.81	**e** 63.1 × 4.18 × 8.32	**f** 320 × 6.95 × 0.98
g 454 ÷ 89.3	**h** 26.8 ÷ 2.97	**i** 4964 ÷ 7.23
j 316 ÷ 3.87	**k** 2489 ÷ 48.58	**l** 63.94 ÷ 8.302

2 Find the approximate monthly pay of the following people with the following annual salaries.
a Joy £47 200 **b** Amy £24 200 **c** Tom £19 135

3 Find the approximate annual pay of these brothers who earn the following amounts.
a Trevor £570 a week **b** Brian £2728 a month

AU **4** A groundsman bought 350 kg of seed at a cost of £3.84 per kg.
a Find the approximate total cost of this seed.
b Did he make a profit?

C

FM **5** A greengrocer sells a box of 250 apples for £47. Approximately how much did each apple sell for?

6 Keith runs about 15 km every day. Approximately how far does he run in:
a a week **b** a month **c** a year?

7 A litre of creosote will cover an area of about 6.8 m^2. Approximately how many litre cans will I need to buy to creosote a fence with a total surface area of 43 m^2?

PS **8** A tour of London sets off at 1013 and costs £21. It returns at 1208.
Approximately how much does the tour cost per hour?

HOMEWORK 14P

D

FM **1** Round each of the following to give sensible answers.
a Kris is 1.6248 metres tall.
b It took me 17 minutes 48.78 seconds to cook the dinner.
c My rabbit weighs 2.867 kg.
d The temperature at the bottom of the ocean is 1.239 °C.
e There were 23 736 people at the game yesterday.

2 How many jars each holding 119 cm^3 of water can be filled from a 3-litre flask?

AU **3** If I walk at an average speed of 62 metres per minute, how long will it take me to walk a distance of 4 km?

FM **4** Helen earns £31 500 a year. She works five days a week for 45 days a year. How much does she earn a day?

5 10 grams of Gold cost £2.17. How much will one kilogram of Gold cost?

FM **6** Rewrite the following article using sensible numbers:
I left home at eleven and a half minutes past two, and walked for 49 minutes.
The temperature was 12.7623 °C. I could see an aeroplane overhead at 2937.1 feet.
Altogether I had walked 3.126 miles.

Functional Maths Activity

Shopping for the elderly

Thelma is a warden for the elderly.
She collects shopping for those who need help.

Harriet, Doris and Wilf are three of the elderly people.

Harriet and Wilf have shopping lists.

Doris is a vegetarian and does not eat meat. She does not have a shopping list.

She gives Thelma £20 and asks her to buy what she can.

Harriet

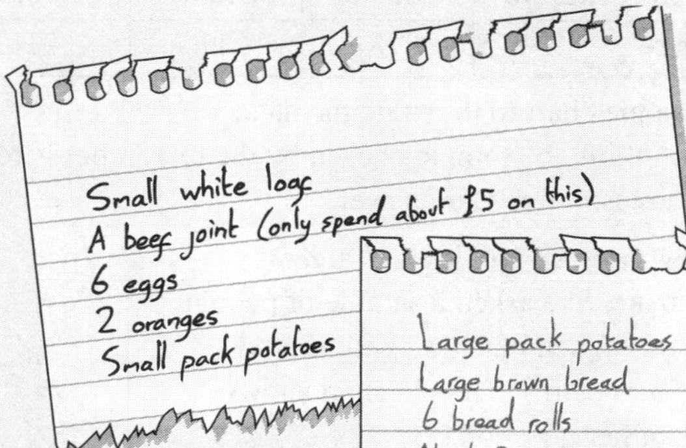

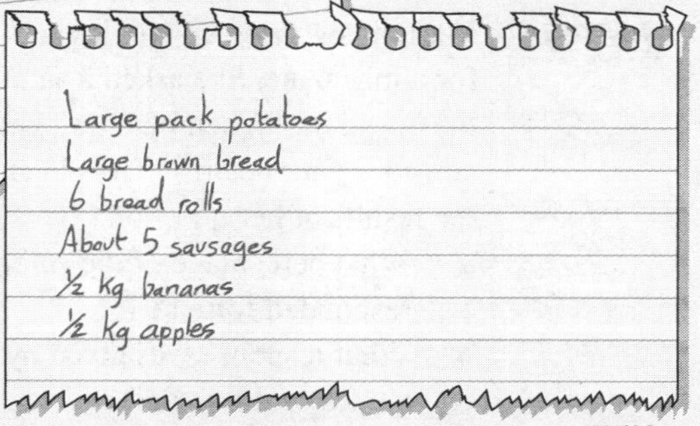

Wilf

Tasks

Work out the costs of Harriet's and Wilf's shopping.
Try to buy a sensible range of food for Doris.
Do not forget that she does not eat meat.
Do not forget you must not spend more than £20.
Show clearly any calculations that you make or any checking that you do.

15 Statistics: Pie charts, scatter diagrams and surveys

15.1 Pie charts

HOMEWORK 15A

E

1 The table shows the time taken by 60 people to travel to work.

Time in minutes	10 or less	Between 10 and 30	30 or more
Frequency	8	19	33

Draw a pie chart to illustrate the data.

2 The table shows the number of GCSE passes that 180 students obtained.

GCSE passes	9 or more	7 or 8	5 or 6	4 or less
Frequency	20	100	50	10

Draw a pie chart to illustrate the data.

3 Tom is doing a statistics project on the use of computers. He decides to do a survey to find out the main use of computers by 36 of his school friends. His results are shown in the table.

Main use	e-mail	Internet	Word processing	Games
Frequency	5	13	3	15

a Draw a pie chart to illustrate his data.
b What conclusions can you draw from his data?
c Give reasons why Tom's data is not really suitable for his project.

4 In a survey, a TV researcher asks 120 people at a leisure centre to name their favourite type of television programme. The results are shown in the table.

Type of programme	Comedy	Drama	Films	Soaps	Sport
Frequency	18	11	21	26	44

a Draw a pie chart to illustrate the data.
b Do you think the sample chosen by the researcher is representative of the population? Give a reason for your answer.

FM 5 Marion is writing an article on health for a magazine. She asked a sample of people the question: 'When planning your diet, do you consider your health?' The pie chart shows the results of her question.

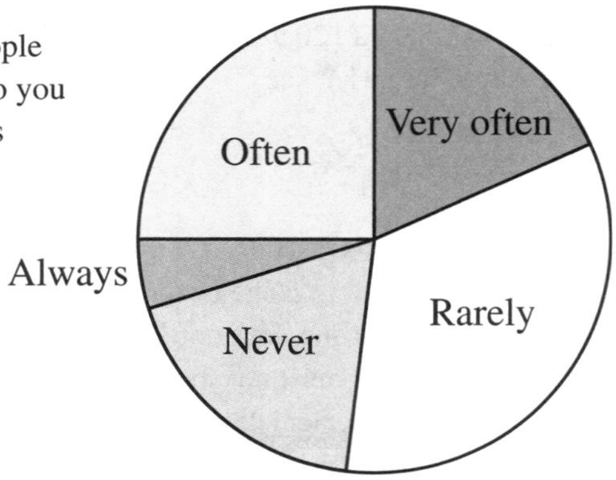

a What percentage of the sample responded 'often'.
b What response was given by about a third of the sample?
c Can you tell how many people there were in the sample? Give a reason for your answer.
d What other questions could Marion ask?

E

PS 6 A nationwide survey was taken on where people thought the friendliest people were in England.
What is the probability that a person picked at random from this survey answered 'East'?

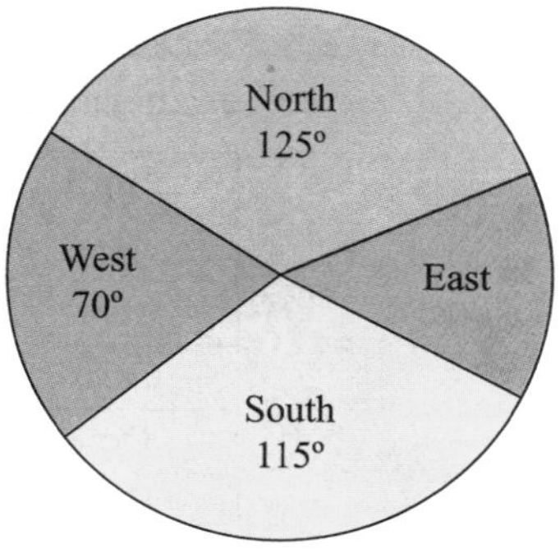

AU 7 You are asked to draw a pie chart representing the different breakfasts that students have in a morning.
What data would you need to obtain in order to do this?

15.2 Scatter diagrams

HOMEWORK 15B

C

1 The table below shows the heights and weights of twelve students in a class.

Student	Weight (Kg)	Height (cm)
Ann	51	123
Bridget	58	125
Ciri	57.5	127
Di	62	128
Emma	59.5	129
Flo	65	129
Gill	65	133
Hanna	65.5	135
Ivy	71	137
Joy	75.5	140
Keri	70	143
Laura	78	145

a Plot the data on a scatter diagram.
b Draw the line of best fit.
c Jayne was absent from the class, but she knows she is 132 cm tall. Use the line of best fit to estimate her weight.
d A new girl joined the class who weighed 55 kg. What height would you expect her to be?

C

FM 2 The table below shows the marks for ten pupils in their mathematics and music examinations.

Pupil	Maths	Music
Alex	52	50
Ben	42	52
Chris	65	60
Don	60	59
Ellie	77	61
Fan	83	74
Gary	78	64
Hazel	87	68
Irene	29	26
Jez	53	45

a Plot the data on a scatter diagram. Take the x-axis for the mathematics scores and mark it from 20 to 100. Take the y-axis for the music scores and mark it from 20 to 100.

b Draw the line of best fit.

c One of the pupils was ill when they took the mathematics examination. Which pupil was it most likely to be?

d Another pupil, Kris, was absent for the music examination but scored 45 in mathematics, what mark would you expect him to have got in music?

e Another pupil, Lex, was absent for the mathematics examination but scored 78 in music, what mark would you expect him to have got in mathematics?

PS 3 Twelve students took part in a maths challenge. The table shows their scores for two tests, a mental test and a problem-solving test.

Mental	25	32	32	43	47	50	55	58	61	65	68	72
Problem	32	30	36	40	50	59	52	53	62	60	48	73

Harry did the mental test and scored 53.
How many marks would you expect him to get in the problem-solving test?

AU 4 Describe what you would expect a scatter graph to look like if someone said that it showed no correlation.

15.3 Surveys

HOMEWORK 15C

C

1 'People like the video rental store to be open 24 hours a day.'

a To see whether this statement is true, design a data collection sheet that will allow you to capture data while standing outside a video rental store.

b Does it matter at which time you collect your data?

2 The youth club wanted to know which types of activities it should plan, e.g. craft, swimming, squash, walking, disco etc.

a Design a data collection sheet that you could use to ask the pupils in your school which activities they would want in a youth club.

b Invent the first 30 entries on the chart.

C

3 What types of film do your age group watch at the cinema the most? Is it comedy, romance, sci-fi, action, suspense or something else?

a Design a data collection sheet to be used in a survey of your age group.

b Invent the first 30 entries on your sheet.

4 Design a two-way table to show the type of music students prefer to listen to in different year groups.

FM 5 Sonia wants to find out who brings packed lunches to school.
She decides to investigate the hypothesis:
'Vegetarians bring packed lunches to school'.

a Design a data capture form that Sonia could use to help her do this.

b Sonia records information from a sample of 50 vegetarians and 40 non-vegetarians. She finds that seven vegetarians and two non-vegetarians brought packed lunch to school.
Based on this sample, is the hypothesis correct?
Explain your answer.

PS 6 How long do students in your school year spend on homework at the weekend?
Design a data collection sheet to assist you find this out.

AU 7 Nusahaa is asked to find out how long people would like the local supermarket to be open for.
She says, 'I will just ask them how long they want it open for.'
What would be the best way for Nusahaa to capture the replies?

HOMEWORK 15D

C

1 Design a questionnaire to test the following statement.
'Young people aged 15 and under will not tell their parents when they have been given a detention at school, but the over 15s will always let their parents know.'

2 'Boys will use the Internet almost every day but girls will only use it about once a week.'
Design a questionnaire to test this statement.

3 Design a questionnaire to test the following hypothesis.
'When you are in your twenties, you watch less TV than any other age group.'

4 While on holiday in Wales, I noticed that in the supermarkets there were a lot more women than men, and the only men I did see were over 65.

a Write down a hypothesis from the above observation.

b Design a questionnaire to test your hypothesis.

C

FM 5 Scott and Gabriel are doing a survey on the type of music 15-year-olds listen to.

a This is one question from Scott's survey.

15-year-olds listen to Pop.		
Don't you agree?		
Strongly agree ☐	Agree ☐	Don't know ☐

Give two criticisms of Scott's question.

b This is a question from Gabriel's survey, which he only asked 15-year-olds.

What kind of music do you prefer to listen to?				
Pop ☐	Rock ☐	Folk ☐	Classical ☐	Other ☐

Give two reasons why this is a good question.

c Make up another good question with responses that could be added to this survey.

PS 6 Design a questionnaire to test the hypothesis:
'People who have "Alexander Lessons" live a healthier life'.

AU 7 Dominic wanted to know how much pocket money students in his school year were getting. He used this questionnaire:

Question:	How much pocket money do you get?			
Response:	Less than £5	☐	Less than £15	☐
	Less than £10	☐	Less than £20	☐

Explain why the response section of this questionnaire is poor.

15.4 The data-handling cycle

HOMEWORK 15E

Use the data-handling cycle to describe how you would test each of the following hypotheses. State in each case whether you would use Primary or Secondary data.

C

1. January is the coldest month of the year.
2. Girls are better than boys at estimating weights.
3. More men go to cricket matches than women.
4. The TV show *Strictly Come Dancing* is watched by more women than men.
5. The older you are the more likely you are to go ballroom dancing.

15.5 Other uses of statistics

HOMEWORK 15F

FM 1 The time series shows washing machine production in the UK from November 2007 to November 2008.

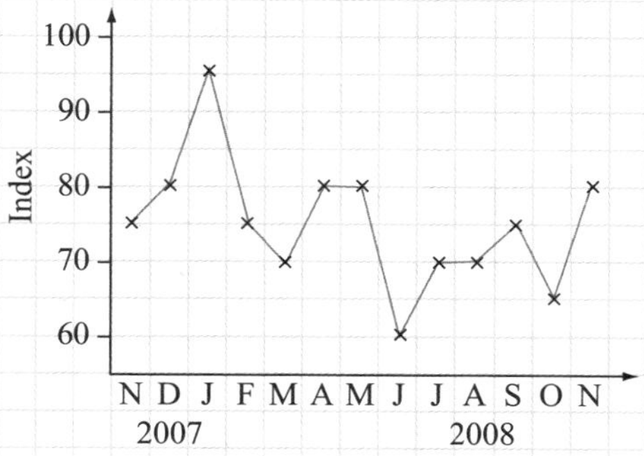

The average production over the first three months shown was 108 000 washing machines.

a Work out an approximate value for the average production over the last three months shown.

b The base month for the index is January 2005, when the index was 100.
What was the approximate production in January 2005?

AU 2 The retail price index measures how much the daily cost of living increases or decreases. If 2009 is given a base index number of 100, and 2010 is given 102, what does this mean?

Functional Maths Activity

Election polls

The UK population was faced with a general election in May 2010, and there were daily polls taken to find out how people intended to vote.

The following polls were recorded on 8th April 2010:

Poll	Labour	Conservative	Liberal Democrat	Other
YouGov %	32	37	19	12
ICM %	33	37	21	9
Mori %	30	35	21	14
Comre %	30	37	20	13

Combine all four polls into a single pie chart that represents the opinion of the UK population on 8th April 2010.

William Collins' dream of knowledge for all began with the publication of his first book in 1819. A self-educated mill worker, he not only enriched millions of lives, but also founded a flourishing publishing house. Today, staying true to this spirit, Collins books are packed with inspiration, innovation and practical expertise. They place you at the centre of a world of possibility and give you exactly what you need to explore it.

Collins. Freedom to teach.

Published by Collins
An imprint of HarperCollins*Publishers*
77–85 Fulham Palace Road
Hammersmith
London
W6 8JB

Browse the complete Collins catalogue at
www.collinseducation.com

10 9 8 7 6 5 4 3 2 1

ISBN-13 978-0-00-734019-4

British Library Cataloguing in Publication Data
A Catalogue record for this publication is available from the British Library

Commissioned by Katie Sergeant
Project managed by Patricia Briggs
Edited by Brian Asbury
Cover design by Angela English
Concept design by Nigel Jordan
Illustrations by Wearset Publishing Services
Typesetting by Wearset Publishing Services
Production by Simon Moore
Printed and bound by L.E.G.O. S.p.A. Italy

Acknowledgement
With thanks to Chris Pearce (Teaching and Learning Advisor, North Somerset).

Important information about the Student Book CD-ROM
The accompanying CD-ROM is for home use only. You cannot copy or save the files to your hard drive and it will work only when placed in the CD-ROM drive.